The Business Environment and Synoptic

Workbook

Published by Osborne Books Limited
Tel 01905 748071
Email books@osbornebooks.co.uk
Website www.osbornebooks.co.uk

Design by Laura Ingham

FSC
www.fsc.org
MIX
Paper | Supporting responsible forestry
FSC® C019717

British Library Cataloguing in Publication Data
A catalogue record for this book is available from the British Library

ISBN 978-1-911198-58-1

Contents

Introduction

Qualifications covered

This book has been written specifically to cover the Unit 'The Business Environment' and the Synoptic Assessment, which are both mandatory for the following qualifications:

AAT Level 2 Certificate in Accounting

AAT Certificate in Accounting – SCQF Level 6

This book contains Chapter Activities which provide extra practice material for the Unit 'The Business Environment' in addition to the activities included in the Osborne Books Tutorial text, and Practice Assessments to prepare the student for the synoptic computer based assessments. The latter are based directly on the structure, style and content of the sample assessment material provided by the AAT at www.aat.org.uk.

Suggested answers to the Chapter Activities and Practice Assessments are set out in this book.

Osborne Study and Revision Materials

Additional materials, tailored to the needs of students studying this unit and revising for the assessment, include:

- **Tutorials:** paperback books with practice activities
- **Wise Guides:** pocket-sized spiral bound revision cards
- **Student Zone:** access to Osborne Books online resources
- **Osborne Books App:** Osborne Books ebooks for mobiles and tablets

Visit www.osbornebooks.co.uk for details of study and revision resources and access to online material.

Chapter
activities

1   An introduction to business

1.1   Provide three types of not-for-profit organisations.

1.2   Indicate in the table below whether the following statements relate to a sole trader or a limited company.

Statement		Sole Trader	Limited Company
(a)	No formal rules to follow		
(b)	Profit taken out of the business in the form of drawings		
(c)	Easy to set up		
(d)	Must follow the rules and regulations set out in the Companies Act 2006		
(e)	More sources of finance available		

1.3   Is a limited company governed by trustees?

Select: | Yes / No |

1.4   Indicate in the table below whether a sole trader, limited company, partnership or charity needs to prepare financial statements in accordance with the Financial Reporting Standards?

(a)	Sole Trader	
(b)	Limited Company	
(c)	Partnership	
(d)	Charity	

1.5   What does the statement of profit and loss show?

(a)	Assets	
(b)	Income	
(c)	Liabilities	
(d)	Expenditure	

Select all that apply.

1.6   What does the statement of financial position show?

(a)	Assets	
(b)	Income	
(c)	Liabilities	
(d)	Expenditure	

Select all that apply.

1.7   Ellie and Cameron run a small business making hand made clothes. They each put £2,000 into the business. They share any decisions, any debts and any profit.

What type of business ownership is this?

(a)	Sole Trader	
(b)	Limited Company	
(c)	Partnership	
(d)	Charity	

1.8   Explain the main difference between a limited company and a public limited company.

1.9   Select the correct answer from the options below.

Statement	
(a) Financial statements should include the personal transactions of the business owner	
(b) A business is treated as separate from its owners	

Select **one** answer.

1.10   Select the type of business that is referred to as an unincorporated business.

(a)	Limited company	
(b)	Partnership	
(c)	Public limited company	
(d)	Sole trader	

Select all that apply.

2 The external business environment

2.1   A product is manufactured in Australia and sold to the UK.

For the British economy is this an example of an export, tariff or import?

(a)	Export	
(b)	Tariff	
(c)	Import	

2.2   Provide examples of two macro-economic factors.

2.3   A manufacturing business relies on overseas suppliers.

(a)   Discuss one risk for this business

(b)   Discuss one uncertainty for this business

2.4   Indicate whether the following statement is true or false.

Statement	True	False
Inflation impacts upon businesses that trade globally		

2.5   Which of the following is a measure of inflation?

(a)	Gross Domestic Product	
(b)	Interest rates	
(c)	Retail Price Index	
(d)	Exchange rates	

Select **one** answer.

2.6   Answer the following statement in relation to the economic cycle.

Statement	Yes	No
Does the current stage of the economic cycle impact upon decisions made by the government?		

2.7   What are the consequences of high unemployment?

(a)	Slow economic growth	
(b)	High economic growth	
(c)	Decrease in consumer spending	
(d)	Increase in consumer spending	

Select all that apply.

2.8   Explain why the government tries to keep levels of employment high.

2.9   What does CPI stand for?

(a)	Consumer Price Index	
(b)	Consumer Product Index	
(c)	Customer Price Index	
(d)	Customer Product Index	

Select the correct option.

2.10   Identify whether the following statements are true or false.

Statement		True	False
(a)	As demand decreases, prices will fall		
(b)	As demand increases, prices will fall		
(c)	As demand increases, prices will rise		
(d)	As demand decreases, prices will rise		

3 Rules and regulations for businesses

3.1 Indicate in the table below whether the following contracts are void, voidable or valid.

Contract		Void	Voidable	Valid
(a)	The buyer was under the influence of alcohol at the time of agreeing the contract			
(b)	A contract was signed to purchase a building			
(c)	A contract in relation to illegal activity			

3.2 Identify the correct meaning of discharge of contract by performance and discharge of contract by breach.

Performance   **Breach**

Both parties have completed their duties that arose from the contract	
This type of discharge allows one party to sue the other party	

3.3 Indicate in the table below whether the following are express or implied terms.

Situation		Express	Implied
(a)	Terms and conditions of the contract are clearly explained		
(b)	The actions of both parties suggest there is a contract		

3.4 Does an invitation to treat constitute an offer?

Select: Yes / No

3.5   Sarah has a Facebook shop and refurbishes old furniture. She has listed a newly refurbished table for £150. Phoebe contacts Sarah and offers £10 less than the advertised price. Sarah states she will accept the offer 'subject to contract'. Jonas then purchases the item at the full listed price of £150. Phoebe is threatening legal action. Was there a contract in place between Sarah and Phoebe?

(a)	There was a contract in place between Sarah and Phoebe because Sarah accepted the offer	
(b)	There was no contract in place because it was implied that there may be further negotiation with the statement 'subject to contract'	

Select the correct answer.

3.6   What is the name of a draft law?

(a)	Bill	
(b)	Act of Parliament	
(c)	Royal Assent	

Select one answer.

3.7   Indicate whether the following statements are true or false in relation to termination of an offer.

Statement		True	False
(a)	The offeror may not revoke the offer		
(b)	A counter offer will terminate the original offer		

3.8   Indicate whether the following statement is true or false.

Statement		True	False
(a)	A sole trader can use the word Ltd after their business name		

3.9   What are the different types of share capital?

3.10   Indicate in the table below which statutory books should be stored by a business.

(a)	Details of customers	
(b)	Details of suppliers	
(c)	Details of directors	
(d)	Details of shareholders	

Select all that apply.

4 The finance function

4.1 Indicate in the table below which tasks impact upon the solvency of the business.

(a)	Banking cheques	
(b)	Bank reconciliation	
(c)	Supplier statement reconciliation	
(d)	Invoicing customers	

Select all that apply.

4.2 Indicate in the table below which of the following tasks are carried out by the finance function.

(a)	Payroll	
(b)	Promoting products and services	
(c)	Sales order processing	
(d)	Recruiting staff	
(e)	Purchasing	

Select all that apply.

4.3 Indicate in the table below which are internal stakeholders of the finance function.

Stakeholder		
(a)	Suppliers	
(b)	Employees	
(c)	Directors	
(d)	Bank	
(e)	Customers	

Select all that apply.

4.4   Identify three ways the finance function within a business provides support to other departments.

4.5   What is the difference between an internal and external auditor?

4.6   Indicate in the table below which tasks are completed by a management accountant and which tasks are completed by a financial accountant.

Task		Management Accountant	Financial Accountant
(a)	Interprets the data and prepares reports for internal use		
(b)	Completes the year-end accounts		
(c)	Completes the year-end tax return		
(d)	Prepares and monitors budgets		

4.7   For a new business starting up, what advice would you give to help it remain solvent?

4.8   What is the difference between efficiency and effectiveness?

5 Financial information and data security

5.1 Identify in the table below which of the following are examples of primary sources of information.

Primary sources	
(a) Articles of Association for a company	
(b) Contract of employment	
(c) Newspaper article about the business	
(d) Accounting text book	

Select all that apply.

5.2 Your colleague, the payroll assistant, is off sick and you urgently need access to the payroll files to run the payroll in her absence. She rings you and tells you to make a note of her user ID and password.

What should you do?

(a)	Take a note of her password and user ID and run the payroll	
(b)	Tell her not to provide you with the details as company policy states user ID and passwords should never be shared	
(c)	Take the details and tell her on this occasion you will run the payroll and will shred the piece of paper the password is written on	

Select the correct option.

5.3   You receive an email that on first glance looks like it is from the IT department. It is saying your account has been compromised and to click on the link to reset your password.

You don't usually receive an email like this and when you hover over the email address it actually shows a different external email address.

What should you do?

(a)	Click on the link and enter your information	
(b)	Forward the email to your manager	
(c)	Report the email to your IT department and delete it	

Select the correct option.

5.4   You receive an email to your work email address from a friend that states she has sent you some photos from your recent weekend away.

Should you click on the attachment?

(a)	Yes, it will be fine, you know where the email has come from	
(b)	No because some attachments can contain viruses	

Select the correct option.

5.5   Select whether the statement is true or false.

Statement	True	False
You should assume information you see on social media is invalid data until you have checked the information for authenticity		

5.6   Select whether the statement is true or false.

Statement	True	False
Monitoring a business's cash position will help maintain the solvency of the business		

5.7 Identify from the table below whether the following are characteristics of manual processes or cloud-based accounting.

		Manual	Cloud-based accounting
(a)	The number of errors may increase		
(b)	The number of errors are minimised		
(c)	Time is saved		
(d)	Time is not saved		
(e)	Reconciliations could be carried out automatically		
(f)	Reconciliations will be carried out by a member of staff		

5.8 What is anti-malware software also known as?

5.9 Select whether the statements are true or false.

Statement		True	False
(a)	A firewall is a virus that can affect computers		
(b)	Phishing is when someone tries to steal data by pretending to be a legitimate business		
(c)	Cyber security aims to protect devices from the threat of viruses and hackers		
(d)	Businesses should use memorable passwords for accessing software		

5.10 List three actions a business can take to reduce the risk of a cyber-attack.

Business communications

6.1 Is information shared externally on an intranet?

Select: | Yes / No |

6.2 Pick the most appropriate email subject line for an email to a supplier regarding a query on an invoice (invoice INV0400) you have received.

Email subject line	
(a) Query regarding invoice INV0400	
(b) Query	
(c) Query regarding invoice	
(d) Invoice	

Select the correct option.

6.3 Indicate from the table below the most appropriate ways of communicating with customers and suppliers.

(a)	Simple words	
(b)	Complicated words to explain your point	
(c)	Short sentences	
(d)	Long sentences	
(e)	Use text slang to make sentences shorter	
(f)	Use abbreviations	

Select all that apply.

6.4 Indicate in the table below whether the following consequences of ineffective and inappropriate communication relate to organisations or individual employees.

(a) Bad press		
(d) Penalties or fines		

6.5 You have been asked to proofread your colleagues email. What key pieces of information are missing?

Hi,

I have only received some of your bank statements. Please send them by Friday otherwise we will not complete them in time.

Kind regards

Tim

6.

Hi Donna,

Jenny said u wanted me to ring a supplier 2 extend payment terms. Do y have there number pls.

Cheers

Carla

_____ use of words.

You are to:

(a) Identify the six incorrect words and enter them in the left-hand column of the table below.

(b) Enter your correction of these six words on the appropriate line in the right-hand column of the table below.

orrect word	ection

(c) Explain why this email is unacceptable.

6.7   You can hear your colleague talking to your manager and hear your name mentioned. However, you are in the middle of talking to a client. What should you do?

(a)	Continue your conversation with the client, giving them your full attention	
(b)	Ask the client to wait a moment and go and speak to your colleague and manager	

Select the correct option.

6.8   'To', 'too' or 'two'?

(a)   Study the three sentences below and tick whether you think they are correct or incorrect.

Sentence		Correct	Incorrect
(a)	There are to many invoices to post		
(b)	I asked my colleague to check an email I wanted to send to a client		
(c)	A too percent trade discount should have been applied to the invoice		

(b)   For any incorrect sentences, please write the correct sentence.

7 Planning and managing your work

7.1 You have lots of tasks to be completed by 2pm today. This is impossible. What action should you take?

(a)	Just work through what you can even though you will not complete everything	
(b)	Speak to your manager to ask what should be prioritised	
(c)	Ask your colleague to complete one of the tasks instead	
(d)	Email the colleagues and managers that have asked you to complete the work to tell them you are too busy	

Select the most appropriate answer.

7.2 What is the difference between a task list and an action plan?

7.3 Explain why is it important to prioritise tasks.

7.4 Classify which tasks fall into these headings.

	Important	**Ad-hoc**	**Urgent**

(a)	Ring a customer back regarding an invoice query which if not resolved will result in the business not being paid	
(b)	Complete this week's payment run	
(c)	Prepare an expenditure report for the production manager	

7.5   Match the planning aid to the activity.

	Diary	**Chart**	**Schedule**
(a)	A visual of the top ten customers		
(b)	Where future appointments are recorded		
(c)	A plan of timings for a staff training day		

7.6   Indicate in the table below whether the following activities are examples of efficiency or courtesy.

Task		**Efficiency**	**Courtesy**
(a)	Politely greet customers		
(b)	Aim to be 100% error free when posting transactions		
(c)	Answer all email within 24 hours		
(d)	Use the customer's name when speaking to them		

7.7   You have a range of tasks to complete. Write a 'to do' list for the rest of Monday. You should prioritise tasks in the order they impact upon the solvency of the business. It is company policy to check the business email account at the beginning of each day. Write the task description in the column on the right. Choose from the following tasks:

Check emails

Process sales invoices

Chase customers with outstanding balances

Bank cheques

Complete supplier reconciliations

Prepare a receivables report for the management meeting at 10am on Tuesday

Prepare a payment run for authorisation on 11am Tuesday

MONDAY 'TO DO' LIST (in order of completion)	
Task 1	
Task 2	
Task 3	
Task 4	
Task 5	

7.8   Indicate in the table below whether the following tasks are routine or non-routine.

Task		Routine	Non-routine
(a)	Weekly sales invoicing		
(b)	Monthly bank reconciliation		
(c)	Check emails daily		
(d)	Arrange a collection for a colleague's birthday		
(e)	Create an ad-hoc sales report		

8 Ethics, sustainability and corporate social responsibility

8.1 Honesty relates to which ethical principle?

(a)	Integrity	
(b)	Objectivity	

Select the correct option.

8.2 This question relates to conflicts of interest.

(a) What is the definition of a conflict of interest?

(b) Give one example of a conflict of interest.

8.3 Completing CPD (Continuing Professional Development) relates to which ethical principle?

(a)	Professional competence and due care	
(b)	Professional behaviour	

Select the correct option.

8.4 Your colleague asks you to change the value on an invoice and process it whilst you wait for a revised invoice to be posted from a supplier.

What action should you take?

(a)	Post the invoice	
(b)	Explain to your colleague you cannot process it and the reason why	

Select the correct option.

8.5   Indicate in the table below whether the following statement is true or false.

Statement	True	False
The Data Protection Act 2018 only relates to records held on a computer		

8.6   A client offers you tickets to see your favourite band. Should you accept them? Explain your answer.

8.7   What are the three pillars of sustainability?

8.8   Is improving the welfare of the workforce part of corporate social responsibility initiatives?

Yes	
No	

8.9   Lisa has nearly completed her AAT qualification and is working in an accounting role. She tells her colleague 'When I have finished my course and I have the letters after my name, I won't need to worry about AAT Code of Professional Ethics'. Is Lisa correct?

(a)	Yes, because she will have completed her qualification	
(b)	No, because whilst an individual works in accounting, the AAT Code of Professional Ethics should always be followed	

Select the most appropriate answer.

8.10   You have just started working in the accounts department of Tino Ltd. Indicate in the table below whether the following statements are true or false in relation to the AAT Code of Professional Ethics.

Statement		True	False
(a)	I don't have to follow the code of ethics as long as Tino Ltd follows them		
(b)	The Code of Ethics refers to how you should behave in your personal life		
(c)	If I don't act ethically in the workplace, this will reflect badly on Tino Ltd		

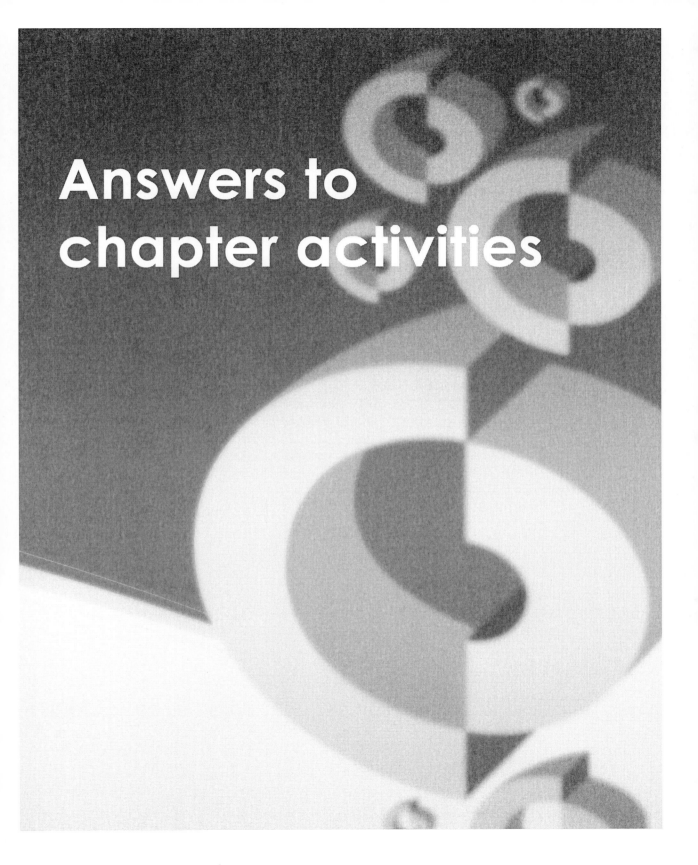

Answers to
chapter activities

CHAPTER 1: AN INTRODUCTION TO BUSINESS

1.1   Charities

Clubs

Public sector

1.2

Statement		Sole Trader	Limited Company
(a)	No formal rules to follow	✔	
(b)	Profit taken out of the business in the form of drawings	✔	
(c)	Easy to set up	✔	
(d)	Must follow the rules and regulations set out in the Companies Act 2006		✔
(e)	More sources of finance available		✔

1.3   No

1.4

(a)	Sole Trader	
(b)	Limited Company	✔
(c)	Partnership	
(d)	Charity	

1.5

(a)	Assets	
(b)	Income	✔
(c)	Liabilities	
(d)	Expenditure	✔

1.6

(a)	Assets	✔
(b)	Income	
(c)	Liabilities	✔
(d)	Expenditure	

1.7

(a)	Sole Trader	
(b)	Limited Company	
(c)	Partnership	✔
(d)	Charity	

1.8   The main difference is that a public limited company's shares can be sold to the general public on the stock exchange when they reach £50,000.

1.9

Statement	
(a) Financial statements should include the personal transactions of the business owner	
(b) A business is treated as separate from its owners	✔

1.10

(a)	Limited company	
(b)	Partnership	✔
(c)	Public limited company	
(d)	Sole trader	✔

CHAPTER 2: THE EXTERNAL BUSINESS ENVIRONMENT

2.1

(a)	Export	✔
(b)	Tariff	
(c)	Import	

2.2   Any two of the following:
  • Competition
  • Reliability of the distribution chain
  • Demand for the business's services or products
  • The size of the market for the services or products

2.3   **(a)**   Any one from the following:
      • Operational risk – for example fraud
      • Financial risk – changes in currencies and interest rates
      • Compliance risk – doing something wrong and facing legal proceedings
      • Competition and reputation risk – new competitors entering the market but also the risk of bad press
  (b)   Political and economic uncertainties - this is outside of our control

2.4

Statement	True	False
Inflation impacts upon businesses that trade globally	✔	

2.5

(a)	Gross Domestic Product	
(b)	Interest rates	
(c)	Retail Price Index	✔
(d)	Exchange rates	

2.6

Statement	Yes	No
Does the current stage of the economic cycle impact upon decisions made by the government?	✔	

2.7

(a)	Slow economic growth	✔
(b)	High economic growth	
(c)	Decrease in consumer spending	✔
(d)	Increase in consumer spending	

2.8 Because unemployment is linked to crime and poor health, and when there are higher levels of unemployment, then the government will need to make more benefit payment.

2.9 Consumer Price Index

2.10

Statement	True	False
(a) As demand decreases, prices will fall	✔	
(b) As demand increases, prices will fall		✔
(c) As demand increases, prices will rise	✔	
(d) As demand decreases, prices will rise		✔

CHAPTER 3: RULES AND REGULATIONS FOR BUSINESSES

3.1

Situation		Void	Voidable	Valid
(a)	The buyer was under the influence of alcohol at the time of agreeing the contract		✔	
(b)	A contract was signed to purchase a building			✔
(c)	A contract in relation to illegal activity	✔		

3.2

Both parties have completed their duties that arose from the contract	**Performance**
This type of discharge allows one party to sue the other party	**Breach**

3.3

Situation		Express	Implied
(a)	Terms and conditions of the contract are clearly explained	✔	
(b)	The actions of both parties suggest there is a contract		✔

3.4   No

3.5

(a)	There was a contract in place between Sarah and Phoebe because Sarah accepted the offer	
(b)	There was no contract in place because it was implied that there may be further negotiation with the statement 'subject to contract'	✔

3.6

(a)	Bill	✔
(b)	Act of Parliament	
(c)	Royal Assent	

3.7

Statement		True	False
(a)	The offeror may not revoke the offer		✔
(b)	A counter offer will terminate the original offer	✔	

3.8

Statement		True	False
(a)	A sole trader can use the word Ltd after their business name		✔

3.9   Ordinary shares and preference shares

3.10

(a)	Details of customers	
(b)	Details of suppliers	
(c)	Details of directors	✔
(d)	Details of shareholders	✔

CHAPTER 4: THE FINANCE FUNCTION

4.1

(a)	Banking cheques	✔
(b)	Bank reconciliation	
(c)	Supplier statement reconciliation	
(d)	Invoicing customers	✔

4.2

(a)	Payroll	✔
(b)	Promoting products and services	
(c)	Sales order processing	✔
(d)	Recruiting staff	
(e)	Purchasing	✔

4.3

Stakeholder		
(a)	Suppliers	
(b)	Employees	✔
(c)	Directors	✔
(d)	Bank	
(e)	Customers	

4.4 Any three from:

- Provides information on customer account balances
- Processes customer orders
- Orders inventory
- Pays for the costs associated with running the business
- Pays employees
- Monitors budgets across the organisation

4.5 An internal auditor is employed by the organisation and their day-to-day role is to check transactions and procedures in place at the business.

An external auditor is not employed by the business and is independent. For larger organisations, external audits are mandatory.

4.6

Task		Management Accountant	Financial Accountant
(a)	Interprets the data and prepares reports for internal use	✔	
(b)	Completes the year-end accounts		✔
(c)	Completes the year-end tax return		✔
(d)	Prepares and monitors budgets	✔	

4.7
- Negotiate credit terms with customers and suppliers. Try and negotiate longer payment terms with suppliers
- Bank cheques immediately
- Monitor inventory purchases
- Prepare a cash flow forecast to ensure they are managing the cash in and out of the business as effectively as possible

4.8 Efficiency is about getting tasks completed in a timely manner, whereas effectiveness is about completing tasks successfully.

CHAPTER 5: FINANCIAL INFORMATION AND DATA SECURITY

5.1

	Primary sources	
(a)	Articles of Association for a company	✔
(b)	Contract of employment	✔
(c)	Newspaper article about the business	
(d)	Accounting text book	

5.2

(a)	Take a note of her password and user ID and run the payroll	
(b)	Tell her not to provide you with the details as company policy states user ID and passwords should never be shared	✔
(c)	Take the details and tell her on this occasion you will run the payroll and will shred the piece of paper the password is written on	

5.3

(a)	Click on the link and enter your information	
(b)	Forward the email to your manager	
(c)	Report the email to your IT department and delete it	✔

5.4

(a)	Yes, it will be fine, you know where the email has come from	
(b)	No because some attachments can contain viruses	✔

5.5 True

5.6 True

5.7

Task		Manual	Cloud-based accounting
(a)	The number of errors may increase	✔	
(b)	The number of errors are minimised		✔
(c)	Time is saved		✔
(d)	Time is not saved	✔	
(e)	Reconciliations could be carried out automatically		✔
(f)	Reconciliations will be carried out by a member of staff	✔	

5.8   Anti-virus software

5.9

Statement		True	False
(a)	A firewall is a virus that can affect computers		✔
(b)	Phishing is when someone tries to steal data by pretending to be a legitimate business	✔	
(c)	Cyber security aims to protect devices from the threat of viruses and hackers	✔	
(d)	Businesses should use memorable passwords for accessing software		✔

5.10   Checking the authenticity of emails received

Do not download files that are from unknown sources

Ensure websites are safe that you are entering personal or sensitive information into

Accept any other valid answer

CHAPTER 6: BUSINESS COMMUNICATIONS

6.1 No, just internally to staff

6.2

Email subject line	
(a) Query regarding invoice INV0400	✔
(b) Query	
(c) Query regarding invoice	
(d) Invoice	

6.3

(a)	Simple words	✔
(b)	Complicated words to explain your point	
(c)	Short sentences	✔
(d)	Long sentences	
(e)	Use text slang to make sentences shorter	
(f)	Use abbreviations	

6.4

Task		Organisation	Individual
(a)	Bad press	✔	
(b)	Loss of profit	✔	
(c)	Lack of promotion		✔
(d)	Penalties or fines	✔	
(e)	Disciplinary action		✔

6.5
- Address the email to the name of client
- Indicate which bank statements are missing
- Add the date for Friday
- Missing bank statements
- Consider rewording in a polite manner 'Please submit by Friday 23 July, otherwise we cannot guarantee that we can submit your accounts to Companies House in time for your year-end filing deadline'.

6.6 **(a)**   **(b)**

Incorrect word	Correction
u	you
2	to
y	you
there	their
pls	please
Cheers	Kind regards

(c)   You should not use slang. This is inappropriate in a professional working environment.

6.7

(a)	Continue your conversation with the client, giving them your full attention	✔
(b)	Ask the client to wait a moment and go and speak to your colleague and manager	

6.8 **(a)**

Sentence		Correct	Incorrect
(a)	There are to many invoices to post		✔
(b)	I asked my colleague to check an email I wanted to send to a client	✔	
(c)	A too percent trade discount should have been applied to the invoice		✔

(b)   (a)   There are **too** many invoices to post

            (c)   A **two** percent trade discount should have been applied to the invoice

CHAPTER 7: PLANNING AND MANAGING YOUR WORK

7.1

(a)	Just work through what you can even though you will not complete everything	
(b)	Speak to your manager to ask what should be prioritised	✔
(c)	Ask your colleague to complete one of the tasks instead	
(d)	Email the colleagues and managers that have asked you to complete the work to tell them you are too busy	

7.2 A task list lists each task that needs to be completed, whereas an action plan is more detailed and may include information such as who is completing the activity and by when.

7.3 Tasks should be prioritised to ensure that vital deadlines are met and that the business is running as efficiently as possible.

7.4

(a)	Ring a customer back regarding an invoice query which if not resolved will result in the business not being paid	**Urgent**
(b)	Complete this week's payment run	**Important**
(c)	Prepare an expenditure report for the production manager	**Ad-hoc**

7.5

(a)	A visual of the top ten customers	**Chart**
(b)	Where future appointments are recorded	**Diary**
(c)	A plan of timings for a staff training day	**Schedule**

7.6

Task		Efficiency	Courtesy
(a)	Politely greet customers		✔
(b)	Aim to be 100% error free when posting transactions	✔	
(c)	Answer all email within 24 hours	✔	
(d)	Use the customer's name when speaking to them		✔

7.7

MONDAY 'TO DO' LIST (in order of completion)	
Task 1	Check emails
Task 2	Bank cheques
Task 3	Chase customers with outstanding balances
Task 4	Process sales invoices
Task 5	Prepare a receivables report for the management meeting at 10am on Tuesday

Note – prioritise tasks on order they impact upon solvency

7.8

Task		Routine	Non-routine
(a)	Weekly sales invoicing	✔	
(b)	Monthly bank reconciliation	✔	
(c)	Check emails daily	✔	
(d)	Arrange a collection for a colleague's birthday		✔
(e)	Create an ad-hoc sales report		✔

CHAPTER 8: ETHICS, SUSTAINABILITY AND CORPORATE SOCIAL RESPONSIBILITY

8.1

(a)	Integrity	✔
(b)	Objectivity	

8.2 **(a)** A conflict of interest is a situation where professional judgment is affected because an individual could benefit personally from a transaction.

(b) For example, accepting a gift from a supplier in return for ensuring their invoice is paid earlier.

8.3

(a)	Professional competence and due care	✔
(b)	Professional behaviour	

8.4

(a)	Post the invoice	
(b)	Explain to your colleague you cannot process it and the reason why	✔

8.5

Statement	True	False
The Data Protection Act 2018 only relates to records held on a computer		✔

8.6 An employee should never accept gifts as this could result in a conflict of interest.

8.7 • Economic growth
• Environmental protection
• Social equality

8.8

Yes	✔
No	

8.9

(a)	Yes, because she will have completed her qualification	
(b)	No, because whilst an individual works in accounting, the AAT Code of Professional Ethics should always be followed	✔

8.10

Statement		True	False
(a)	I don't have to follow the code of ethics as long as Tino Ltd follows them		✔
(b)	The Code of Ethics refers to how you should behave in your personal life	✔	
(c)	If I don't act ethically in the workplace, this will reflect badly on Tino Ltd	✔	

Practice synoptic assessment 1

Information

The total time for this practice assessment is two hours.

The total mark for this practice assessment is 100.

There are eight tasks to be completed and you should complete every question.

The marks for each sub-task are shown alongside the task.

Read each task carefully before attempting the questions.

The VAT rate is 20%.

Task 1: 10 marks

This task tests your understanding of the setting up of different types of entities.

(a)   Indicate in the table below whether the following statements are true or false.

Statement	True	False
A sole trader is also referred to as 'self-employed'		
Income Tax applies to individuals only		
Corporation Tax applies to partnerships only		

(3 marks)

(b)   A friend is looking to set up a limited company with her colleague and asks your advice. Advise your friend by selecting whether the following statements are true or false.

Statement	True	False
You will need to identify and decide who will be classed as 'people with significant control' (PSC) over your business		
You can choose any business name		
You should have one guarantor and one shareholder		
You should choose a director of the company who can also be a shareholder		

(4 marks)

(c)   When purchasing an 'off the shelf' company, which two of the following statements are correct?

(a)	You can choose the company name	
(b)	All legal documents are provided	
(c)	Quicker to set up	

(2 marks)

(d) Indicate in the table below which of the following stakeholders of a finance department is classed as external?

Stakeholder	
(a) HM Revenue & Customs	
(b) Directors	
(c) Staff	

(1 mark)

Task 2: 13 marks

This task relates to the finance function, the information requirements, and its role in the wider organisation.

You work from 09.00 to 14.00, Monday to Friday of each week. Each finance period is four weeks in duration so you plan your work in a four week cycle.

The work schedules below show the days when routine tasks must be completed and the amount of time each task takes to complete. It is very important that you complete the management accounts tasks by the end of the identified day and the financial accounts tasks by the day and time indicated.

Monthly work schedule – management accounts					
	Monday	**Tuesday**	**Wednesday**	**Thursday**	**Friday**
Week 1	Data gathering (3 hours)	Cost coding (1 hour)			
Week 2		Labour cost report (1 hour)	Labour cost report (1 hour)	Labour cost report (1 hour)	
Week 3	Budget report (2 hours)		Material cost report (2 hours)		
Week 4			Product cost analysis (1 hour)	Product cost analysis (1 hour)	Variance analysis (2 hours)

Weekly work schedule – financial accounts			
Task	**Task to be completed each week by:**		**Task duration**
	Day	**Time**	
Contact customers	Wednesday	13:00	2 hours
Contact suppliers	Tuesday	11:00	1 hour
Process purchase invoices	Tuesday	14:00	2 hours
Check emails and post cheques	Every day	12:00	1 hour
Prepare payments to suppliers	Friday	10:00	1 hour
Reconcile supplier statements	Thursday	14:00	2 hours
Process sales invoices	Monday	14:00	2 hours

You are planning your work at the start of the day on Thursday of week 2. You have been asked to complete a non-routine petty cash book task by 10am, which is already on your to-do list.

(a) Complete your to-do list for today, Thursday of week 2. Refer to the management and financial accounts schedules and list the tasks in order of completion in the table set out below. Write the task descriptions in the column on the right. You can see the list has been started for you.

Choose from the following tasks:

Contact customers	Data gathering
Product cost analysis	Cost coding
Budget report	Prepare payments to suppliers
Contact suppliers	Variance analysis
Process purchase invoices	Process sales invoices
Labour cost report	Material cost report
Check emails and post cheques	Reconcile supplier statements

Thursday, week 2 to-do list (in order of completion)	
Task 1 09.00 - 10.00	Petty cash book
Task 2 10.00 - 11.00	
Task 3 11.00 - 12.00	
Task 4 12.00 - 13.00	
Task 5 13.00 - 14.00	

(4 marks)

You are often asked to complete non-routine tasks. However, on one day in each of the four week cycles, you are too busy with routine tasks to accept non-routine work.

(b)   Identify on which day in which week you will be the busiest with routine tasks from the management and financial accounts schedules. Enter your answer into the table below.

Week number	Day of the week

(2 marks)

There are a number of tasks that colleagues complete.

(c)   Match the task with the job role.

Task	**Job role**
Sales figures report for each sales advisor	Sales Manager
Production schedule for the factory	Human Resources Assistant
Process invoices received from suppliers	Receivables Ledger Assistant
Process cheques received	Production Manager
Prepare employee contracts	Cashier
	Payables Ledger Assistant

(5 marks)

(d)   Indicate from the table below which department will need the following information.

	Sales	Marketing
The cost of promoting goods for sale on Facebook		
The revenue generated from sales received through Facebook advertisements		

(2 marks)

Task 3: 14 marks

This task is about ethics, sustainability and corporate social responsibility (CSR).

JYB Supplies is reviewing its sustainability policy.

(a)   Select which areas of sustainability the following statements refer to.

	Social	**Environmental**
Using resources that can be reused		
Supporting colleagues		
Reduction of emissions		
Reducing the quantity of printing		
Donation of profits to charity		
Offering a cycle to work incentive scheme		
Energy saving schemes		

(7 marks)

(b)   Match the ethical principle to the situation. Choose from the following principles: Confidentiality, Objectivity, Integrity, Professional competence and due care, Professional behaviour.

Situation	**Ethical principle**
Your colleague asks you whether you are working on their parent's accounts and to tell them whether they made a profit in the year	
Your manager is off sick. Your colleague needs you to complete a tax return. You have never received training as to how to complete a tax return	
You are responsible for collating monthly expense receipts. Your colleague said they left a receipt for work travel at a friend's house and can you process it and they will pass you the receipt next week	

(3 marks)

(c)   You are talking to you colleague about confidentiality.

Indicate from the table below whether the following statement is true or false.

	True	**False**
It is never acceptable in any circumstance to disclose confidential information		

(1 mark)

(d)   Select whether the following statements are true or false.

	True	False
If a business adopts sustainable measures, it will save money		
Moving to cloud-based accounting and not printing invoices and purchase orders is a sustainable measure		
Government schemes are available to help towards the cost of businesses reducing emissions		

(3 marks)

Task 4: 22 marks

This task is about processing transactions and communicating with suppliers.

JYB Supplies has purchased goods from Light Ltd and has received an invoice. It also received a credit note as some faulty goods were returned.

(a) Check the invoice below and credit note on the next page for accuracy.

(4 marks)

Purchase Invoice

INVOICE

Light Limited
250 Lenton Boulevard
Clifton, CL45 5KG

VAT Reg GB 541 4874 56

invoice to							
JYB Supplies			invoice no		96532		
410 Wrenthorpe Industrial Estate			date/tax point		12 July 20-X		
Clifton							
CL47 6KU							

Product Code	Description	Quantity	Price	Unit	Total	Discount	Net
MEB5	**Matt Emulsion Paint – Blue 5L**	70	**£7.50**	**each**	**£525.00**	**20%**	**£420.00**

terms		net total	525.00
Net monthly		VAT	84.00
Carriage paid		TOTAL	441.00
E & OE			

Errors on purchase invoice ....

Purchase credit note

CREDIT NOTE

Light Limited
250 Lenton Boulevard
Clifton, CL45 5KG

VAT Reg GB 541 4874 56

invoice to			
JYB Supplies		credit note no	CN 2044
410 Wrenthorpe Industrial Estate		date/tax point	25 July 20-X
Clifton			
CL47 6KU			

Product Code	Description	Quantity	Price	Unit	Total	Discount	Net
MEB5	Matt Emulsion Paint – Blue 5L	12	£7.50	each	£90.00	20%	£81.00

	net total	81.00
Reason for credit: 2 faulty	VAT	16.20
	TOTAL	97.20

Errors on purchase credit note ....

Your next task is to enter the invoices that follow into the digital bookkeeping system. Your manager has checked the invoices for accuracy and is happy they are all correct. You are informed that the supplier code for PWS Supplies is PW001 and the supplier code for Working Products is WO001 and that these invoices should be coded to general purchases 5000.

(b)   Highlight which module option in the digital bookkeeping system the invoices should be recorded in by ticking the correct option.

(a)	Sales daybook	
(b)	Sales returns daybook	
(c)	Purchases daybook	
(d)	Purchase returns daybook	

(1 mark)

Purchase Invoice

INVOICE

PWS Supplies
41 Carlthon Hill
Burton BF4 7HY
VAT Reg GB 748 5410 01

invoice to		
JYB Supplies	invoice no	INV4514
410 Wrenthorpe Industrial Estate	date/tax point	29 July 20-X
Clifton		
CL47 6KU		

Product Code	Description	Quantity	Price	Unit	Total	Discount	Net
ST012	**Step ladder (3 treads)**	**12**	**12.20**	**each**	**146.40**	**15%**	**124.44**

terms

Net monthly	**net total**	124.44
Carriage paid	**VAT**	24.88
E & OE	**TOTAL**	149.32

Purchase Invoice

INVOICE

Working Products
58 Granby Road
Burton BG5 4DS
VAT Reg GB 236 02455 87

invoice to		
JYB Supplies	invoice no	269852
410 Wrenthorpe Industrial Estate	date/tax point	30 July 20-X
Clifton		
CL47 6KU		

Product Code	Description	Quantity	Price	Unit	Total	Discount	Net
WPM24	**Work platform - medium**	**30**	**£18.30**	**each**	**£549.00**	**10%**	**494.10**

terms

Net monthly	**net total**	494.10
Carriage paid	**VAT**	98.82
E & OE	**TOTAL**	592.92

(c)   Make the entries into the digital bookkeeping system below. The first line has been partially completed for you.

Date 20-X	Supplier code	Supplier	General ledger code	Invoice number	Net £	VAT code
29 July	PW001	PWS Suppliers				

(11 marks)

VAT code options:

V1 – Exempt

V2 – 0%

V3 – 5%

V4 – 20%

The Finance Manager, Tina Brett, has left you the following note today, 2 June 20-X, in relation to a customer:

Note

I am concerned that the balance on the account of Carlton Homeworld has been overdue for 60 days. We offer strict credit terms of 30 days.

Please can you prepare a letter for me to sign, addressed to Mr Jones at Homeworld, requesting payment of £9,500 in relation to invoice 451 dated 1 April 20-X.

Please explain the situation and ask for payment by return. If he has any queries, please ask him to contact me directly.

Thank you

Tina

(d) Prepare an appropriate business letter to Carlton Homeworld, making sure all the relevant information is included from the note above.

JYB Supplies
410 Wrenthorpe Industrial Estate
Clifton, CL47 6KU

Mr Jones
Carlton Homeworld
Newmarket Lane
Burton
BF5 8JK

(6 marks)

Task 5: 10 marks

This task is about using journals, control accounts and reconciliations.

At the end of May you have partially prepared JYB Supplies' payables ledger control account, as shown below.

Payables ledger control

Details	Amount £	Details	Amount £
Bank	4,630	Balance b/d	5,410

You now have the totals of the purchase and purchase returns day books and must record the appropriate amounts in the payables ledger control account.

Purchase daybook extract

Date 20-X	Details	Total £	VAT £	Net £
May	Total	5,448	908	4,540

Purchase returns daybook extract

Date 20-X	Details	Total £	VAT £	Net £
May	Total	960	160	800

(a) What will the entries be into the payables ledger control account?

Account name	Amount £	Debit	Credit
Entry from the purchase daybook			
Entry from the purchase returns daybook			

(4 marks)

(b) What will the balance carried down in the payables ledger control account be?

Amount £	Debit	Credit

(2 marks)

Your next task is to reconcile the receivables with the balance in the receivables ledger control account. These are the balances in the receivables ledger on 1 June.

Credit customers	Balances	
	Amount £	Debit/Credit
Carlton Homeworld	9,500	Debit
TYS Supplies	2,510	Credit
Timber plc	1,440	Debit
JB & Son Painters	3,660	Debit
TS Newton	16,926	Debit

You have inserted the balance of the receivables ledger control account in the reconciliation statement below.

(c) Complete the reconciliation statement by:

- inserting the total of the balances in the receivables ledger

- calculating any difference

Reconciliation statement	Amount £
Receivables ledger control account balance	29,463
Total of the receivables ledger balances	
Difference	

(2 marks)

Your supervisor wants to know what may have caused the difference shown in the reconciliation statement.

(d) Which **two** of the reasons below could explain the difference you calculated in (c) above?

Reasons	
A discount allowed was not entered in a customer's account in the receivables ledger	
A credit note was entered twice in the receivables ledger control account	
An invoice was entered twice in a customer's account in the receivables ledger	
A discount allowed was entered twice in the receivables ledger control account	
A receipt was entered twice in a customer's account in the receivables ledger	
An invoice was entered twice in the receivables ledger control account	

(2 marks)

Task 6: 7 marks

This task relates to contract law.

(a)   Indicate in the table below whether the following relate to civil law or criminal law.

	Civil law	Criminal law
Fraud		
Money laundering		
Breach of contract		

(3 marks)

(b)   Indicate in the table below whether the following statements are true or false.

	True	False
An invitation to treat is an offer		
A valid contract is legally binding		
A void contract can be enforced by law		

(3 marks)

Josie advertised her car for sale on Facebook for £4,000. Jasmin saw Josie's post and messaged Josie to say she would like to buy the car for £4,000. Josie ignored Jasmin's message and sold the car to Tim for £4,400.

(c)   Indicate in the table below whether there is a valid contract in place between Josie and Jasmin.

(a)	Yes, because the message had been sent to Josie and Josie should have acknowledged it	
(b)	No, because Josie did not reply to Jasmin's offer and therefore did not accept it	
(c)	Yes, because Josie should have told Jasmin she was not accepting the offer	

(1 mark)

Task 7: 10 marks

This task relates to data security and bookkeeping systems.

Nathan is a personal trainer, travelling to his clients' homes to deliver training sessions. He uses a cloud-based app on his mobile phone to log how many business miles he is travelling and to invoice clients after each session.

Nathan decided not to add two-step security verification to his phone as it was too time consuming. He also holds his clients' personal details on his phone.

The following week his phone is stolen.

(a) State the implications for his business and the steps he should take to avoid this happening again.

(5 marks)

Nathan has a spreadsheet that contains his clients' personal details, including how much each client has spent in the past year, that he needs to email to his accountant.

(b) Which of the following would be most appropriate when emailing his accountant to protect the data?

(a)	Email the file as it is	
(b)	Password protect the file with a filename that is easy to remember such as 123	
(c)	Password protect the file with a password that contains a combination of upper and lower case letters and symbols	

(1 mark)

Rakesh runs a small cupcake business and has taken on his first employee. The employee will be baking and purchasing ingredients. The cloud-based accounting system allows Rakesh to add an employee to the software.

(c)   How does having the new employee added and able to access the accounting software help the business?

(3 marks)

You work for TKA Ltd. Within the Credit Control Department, you have been asked to chase outstanding customer payments. When you phone David at Jonathan & Son Ltd, he tells you they will make payment but they are awaiting payment from a customer who your company also deals with, called BHY & Son, and asks you for the Director's personal mobile number as this will mean they can pay your bill quicker.

(d)   Identify what action you should take.

(a)	Give him the Director's work mobile number instead	
(b)	Give him the number to ensure the company gets paid	
(c)	Give out the email address instead	
(d)	Refer to your supervisor as this is confidential information you are being asked to disclose	

(1 mark)

Task 8: 14 marks

This task is about the external business environment.

(a)   Lower taxes can increase consumer spending?

(a) Yes	
(b) No	

(1 mark)

(b)   In relation to the global market, indicate in the table below whether the following statements are true or false.

Statement	True	False
The threat of fraud is an example of a compliance risk		
Political uncertainties are outside of our control		
Changes in interest rates is an example of a political risk		
Facing legal proceedings is an example of compliance risk		

(4 marks)

(c)   Is an upturn of the economy known as a boom or a recession?

(a) Boom	
(b) Recession	

(1 mark)

(d)   Indicate in the table below whether the following statement is true or false.

Statement	True	False
A trade deficit occurs when imports exceed exports		

(1 mark)

(e)   Indicate in the table below the consequence of high unemployment.

(a)	Slow economic growth	
(b)	Increase in consumer spending	

(1 mark)

(f)   Indicate in the table below whether the following statements are true or false.

Statement	True	False
High inflation results in consumers spending less		
Deflation is often referred to as negative inflation		

(2 marks)

(g)   Indicate in the table below whether the following statements are true or false in relation to internal and external risks faced by businesses.

Statement	True	False
Technology issues relating to not keeping software up-to-date is an internal risk to the business		
Labour shortages due to not having the correctly skilled workforce is an external risk		
New technology that could make your business's technology obsolete is an example of an external risk		
Fluctuations in exchange rates is an example of an external risk		

(4 marks)

Practice synoptic assessment 2

Information

The total time for this practice assessment is two hours.

The total mark for this practice assessment is 100.

There are eight tasks to be completed and you should complete every question.

The marks for each sub-task are shown alongside the task.

Read each task carefully before attempting the questions.

The VAT rate is 20%.

Task 1: 10 marks

This task tests your understanding of the different types of entities.

(a)   Indicate in the table below whether the following statements relate to a sole trader, limited company, partnership or a not-for-profit.

		Sole Trader	Limited Company	Partnership	Not-for-profit
(a)	Difficult to take time off				
(b)	Shares the profit and responsibilities				
(c)	Controlled by shareholders				
(d)	Set up to make a difference rather than make a profit				
(e)	With this ownership, if the owner is ill, the business may have to cease trading				

(5 marks)

(b)   Indicate in the table below whether the following statements are true or false.

		True	False
(a)	A pre-incorporation contract is a contract entered into before a company has been legally formed		
(b)	A pre-incorporation contract must be in writing		

(2 marks)

(c)   Your friend has set up a new limited company and advises you of the following information. Indicate in the table below whether the following statements are correct or incorrect.

Statement		Correct	Incorrect
(a)	If I convert to a limited company from a sole trader, I will have to pay Corporation Tax through my business		
(b)	I will need directors and shareholders		
(c)	Shareholders will not have limited liability		

(3 marks)

Task 2: 13 marks

This task is about the finance function of businesses.

You have been asked to explain the importance of solvency to your colleague, Tamara.

(a)   Which of the following tasks affect the solvency of the business?

(a)	Stock valuation	
(b)	Chasing customers for payment	
(c)	Banking cheques received	
(d)	Being able to work to deadlines	

(2 marks)

(b)   If the business wants to improve the working capital position, which option would you choose?

(a)	Customers pay earlier	
(b)	Take advantage of any cash discounts offered	
(c)	Not take advantage of any prompt payments offered	
(d)	Pay the National Insurance Contributions of employees to HMRC earlier	
(e)	Pay suppliers earlier	

(1 mark)

(c)   Identify which of the following improves the smooth running of an organisation, improves solvency or is a legal requirement.

(7 marks)

| A sustainability policy including details of the new car sharing scheme |

smooth running of an organisation

| Petty cash procedures |

| Making sure credit customers pay on time |

| Electronic planner of staff holidays to ensure staff absences are evenly spread |

improves solvency

| Paying the PAYE and National Insurance Contributions to HMRC |

| Paying VAT due |

is a legal requirement

| Avoiding having to pay overtime to staff |

(d)   Your manager is delivering some training in relation to the financial stability of the business.

Identify which of the following activities will impact upon the long-term financial stability of the business.

(a)	Meeting tax deadlines	
(b)	Not keeping the payroll records up-to-date	
(c)	Knowing the day-to-day running costs of the business	
(d)	Completing a Microsoft Excel course	

(2 marks)

(e)   A business has one member of staff responsible for the payroll function. She has handed in her notice with immediate effect. Usually, each month the payroll and processing of timesheets is extremely time-consuming. The payroll administrator usually worked overtime to get everything completed by deadlines and there were often mistakes made.

Identify the best course of action for the business to take.

(a)	Promote someone from within the business by advertising the role internally	
(b)	Advertise the post externally	
(c)	Outsource the payroll function to a specialist company	

(1 mark)

Task 3: 14 marks

This task is about ethics, sustainability, and corporate social responsibility (CSR).

Brooklane Ltd is trying to become a more sustainable company.

(a)   From the list below, what would improve sustainability?

(a)	Driving for two hours to attend a meeting	
(b)	Holding a meeting via skype	
(c)	Using recyclable plant holders	
(d)	Ensuring customers are treated equally	
(e)	Promoting a cycle to work scheme	
(f)	Printing all accounting correspondence and filing in the accounts office	

(3 marks)

(b)   Which three are fundamental principles of ethics in the workplace?

(a)	Integrity	
(b)	Objectivity	
(c)	Confidence	
(d)	Effectiveness	
(e)	Professional competence and due care	
(f)	Motivation	

(3 marks)

At Steinbeck Storage Solutions, management are very conscious of wanting to ensure they promote sustainability. You are asked to look at the following list.

(c)   Identify which **four** of the following would improve sustainability.

(a)	Not providing the time off for a member of staff to attend an AAT course	
(b)	Sponsoring a local charity bike ride	
(c)	Buying supplies from the cheapest supplier possible	
(d)	Recycling packaging used on deliveries	
(e)	Restricting the use of the internet at work for social networking	
(f)	Allowing staff time off to volunteer at the local school summer fayre	
(g)	Running the heating at a low level all year	

(4 marks)

(d)   Complete the following sentences in relation to acting ethically by filling in the missing words.

An accounting technician should comply with the AAT's Code of ....

An accounting technician has a .... to their employer, clients and society.

Complying with .... may not constitute ethical behaviour.

Choose from:
Integrity
Professional ethics
Regulations
Public interest duty

(3 marks)

You have started as an accounts assistant at Carlton Ltd and are being trained on how to process the expenses and check each claim. You notice that your colleague (who is also the Finance Director's son) is claiming mileage to and from work every day. You mention this to your line manager who jokes 'you try telling the boss he can't claim it – I suppose it depends whether you want to stay working here'. You politely speak to the Finance Director who tells you to 'post the transactions'.

(e)   What action should you take?

(a)	Process the transaction as without this job you cannot pay your mortgage	
(b)	Contact the AAT for advice	
(c)	Speak to your colleague who has been claiming the mileage	

(1 mark)

Task 4: 22 marks

This task is about processing transactions and communicating with suppliers.

The Finance Manager, Chris Brian, has left you the following note today 3 July 20-X:

Note

Please can you prepare a letter for me to sign, addressed to Mr Templin, the owner of Sleaford Supplies.

I would like you to query credit note 542 dated 27 June 20-X. The credit note states one return but we returned two sets of garden furniture on 20 June 20-X.

The credit note has also been omitted from the statement we have just received from Mr Templin dated 30 June 20-X.

Please explain the situation and ask for the credit note and statement to be reissued and any queries, please ask him to contact me directly.

Thank you

Chris

(a) Prepare an appropriate business letter to Sleaford Supplies, making sure all the relevant information is included from the note above.

Brooklane Garden Centre
28 Steinbeck Street
Granby, BG3 8JY

Mr Templin
Sleaford Supplies
Coulby Lane
Granby
BH8 5GH

(6 marks)

Your next task is to enter the documents below into the appropriate daybook. Your manager has checked the documents for accuracy and is happy they are all correct.

(b)   Highlight which module option in the digital bookkeeping system the credit notes should be recorded in by ticking the correct option.

(a)	Sales daybook	
(b)	Purchase returns daybook	
(c)	Purchases daybook	
(d)	Sales returns daybook	

(1 mark)

Purchase credit note

CREDIT NOTE

Woodborough Ltd
60 Newmarket Lane
Wollaton, WL5 2JP

VAT Reg GB 697 7840 74

invoice to

Steinbeck Storage Solutions	credit note no	CN 067
53 Maclean Industrial Estate	date/tax point	30 July 20-X
Beeston		
BH6 5RS		

Product Code	Description	Quantity	Price	Unit	Total	Discount	Net
MEB5	**Hardwood**	**10**	**£17.50**	**each**	**£175**	**20%**	**£140.00**

	net total	£140.00
Reason for credit	**VAT**	£28.00
wrong type of wood issued	**TOTAL**	£168.00

Purchase credit note

CREDIT NOTE

LYB Newton & Son Ltd
47 Stockhill Lane
Bramcote, BR45 7UE

VAT Reg GB 201 7036 01

invoice to	
Steinbeck Storage Solutions	credit note no 01240
53 Maclean Industrial Estate	date/tax point 31 July 20-X
Beeston	
BH6 5RS	

Product Code	Description	Quantity	Price	Unit	Total	Discount	Net
CAB451	Small cabinets	6	£163.20	each	£979.20	20%	£783.36

net total	£783.36
VAT	£156.67
TOTAL	£940.03

Reason for credit
damaged during transit

(c) Make the entries into the digital bookkeeping system below. You are informed that the supplier code for Woodborough Ltd is WDB012 and the supplier code for LYB Newton & Son Ltd is YNS002, and that the general ledger code for purchases is 5012 and for purchase returns is 5013.

Date 20-X	Supplier code	Supplier	General ledger code	Credit note number	Net £	VAT code
		Totals				

(14 marks)

VAT code options:

V1 – Exempt

V2 – 0%

V3 – 5%

V4 – 20%

(d)   Match the following documents to the appropriate daybooks:

Document

Daybook

| Sales daybook |

| Invoice issued to a credit customer |

| Purchase returns daybook |

| Cash book |

| Invoice received from a supplier |

| Sales returns daybook |

| Purchases daybook |

(1 mark)

Task 5: 10 marks

This task is about using journals, control accounts and reconciliations.

(a) Brooklane Garden Centre has just been informed that a credit customer, Murray Ltd, has ceased trading.

Here is Murray Ltd's account in the receivables ledger; all amounts include VAT at 20%.

Murray Ltd

Date 20-X	Details	Amount £	Date 20-X	Details	Amount £
1 July	Balance b/f	960.50	14 July	Credit note 0236	65.80
16 July	Invoice 2546	2,478.90			
17 July	Invoice 2590	205.70			

(1) Use the journal to record the entries in the general ledger to write off the net amount, VAT amount and the total amount.

Journal

Account name	Amount £	Debit	Credit

(3 marks)

(2) Show whether the errors below will cause an imbalance in the trial balance.

	Will cause an imbalance	Will not cause an imbalance
The vehicle expenses have been debited with £12,451. This should have been posted to the vehicles account		
The balance on the rent received account has been calculated incorrectly		

(2 marks)

(b)   On 31 July a partially completed trial balance had a credit balance of £90,620 and a debit balance of £102,649.

The accounts below have not been entered into the trial balance. Complete the table below to show whether each balance will be a debit or a credit in the trial balance.

Account name	Original balance £	Debit	Credit
Purchase returns	2,906		
VAT Control (owing to HMRC)	5,680		
Bank interest received	58		
Bank (overdrawn bank balance)	3,970		
Sales returns	585		

(5 marks)

Task 6: 7 marks

This task relates to contract law.

(a)   Indicate in the table below whether the following statements relate to common law or equity.

		Common law	Equity
(a)	The only possible remedy is damages		
(b)	Concerned about fairness		
(c)	Introduced remedies such as injunctions		

(3 marks)

(b)   Indicate in the table below whether the following statements relate to public law or private law.

		Public law	Private law
(a)	This law deals with matters such as social welfare across the UK		
(b)	This law focuses on enforcing the law between individuals		
(c)	This law can include company law		

(3 marks)

Your friend runs an IT repair centre. You mention that your computer won't switch on. He says he will take a look and you drop your laptop off with him. He tells you it's fixed and when you return presents you with an invoice for £200.

(c)   Is there a contract?

(a)	Yes	
(b)	No	

(1 mark)

Task 7: 10 marks

This task relates to data security and bookkeeping systems.

Tim runs a garage. The accountant hasn't yet provided him with the final accounts that he needs for an urgent meeting with the bank.

(a) Which characteristic of useful information applies to this situation?

(a)	Timely	
(b)	Comparable	
(c)	Consistent	
(d)	Relevant	

(1 mark)

Leila has no experience of accountancy and has just started as an accounts trainee.

(b) Match the document to the description.

		Purchase order	Statement	Remittance advice	Invoice
(a)	This is completed when goods are ordered				
(b)	This advises when payment is made				
(c)	This shows how much money is owed at the end of month				
(d)	This shows how much is owed for a specific order and the date it should be paid				

(4 marks)

A client uses an app to record their accounting information. You see a post on social media to say that the app has had a data breach.

(c) What action should you take?

(a)	Check the app developer's website	
(b)	Notify the client	
(c)	Speak to your manager	
(d)	Ignore it as it may be fake news	
(e)	Suggest a new software	

(2 marks)

A new business asks your advice about ensuring information and data is retained securely as it will need to use accounting software and store customer information.

(d) What are the top three things you would suggest to the business?

(a)	Make sure passwords are memorable and simple to remember such as your date of birth	
(b)	Everyone should have access to the whole computer system	
(c)	The cloud will automatically back up your PC	
(d)	You will need to ensure that each software you use is backed up	
(e)	You should use passwords that contain a mixture of upper case, lower case, letters, numbers and special characters	
(f)	You should restrict staff access to the areas they need to use in the software they have access to	

(3 marks)

Task 8: 14 marks

This task is about the external business environment.

(a)   Indicate in the table below whether the following statements are true or false.

		True	False
(a)	If Gross Domestic Product (GDP) increases, the standard of living should improve		
(b)	If Gross Domestic Product (GDP) increases, this is a sign of economic strength		
(c)	If exports exceed imports, there will be a trade deficit		

(3 marks)

(b)   Indicate in the table below which of the following are principles of a good tax system.

(a)	Fairness	
(b)	Efficiency	
(c)	Convenience	
(d)	Effectiveness	

(2 marks)

(c)   Indicate in the table below whether the following taxes are direct or indirect.

		Direct	Indirect
(a)	Income Tax		
(b)	Inheritance Tax		
(c)	Council Tax		

(3 marks)

(d)   Match the statements to the various elements of the economic cycle.

		Boom	Recession	Slowdown	Recovery
(a)	Where GDP is in decline for two consecutive quarters				
(b)	An upturn in the economy				
(c)	The stage of the economic cycle that follows recession				
(d)	When the rate of the economic growth decelerates				

(4 marks)

(e)   Answer the following two questions in relation to the economic environment.

	Increased	Decreased
If the demand for expensive items increases and there is a decrease in demand for basic items, does this mean consumer income has increased or decreased?		

(1 mark)

	Strong currency	Weak currency
If a business finds imports are more expensive than exports, this is a sign of what?		

(1 mark)

Practice synoptic assessment 3

Information

The total time for this practice assessment is two hours.

The total mark for this practice assessment is 100.

There are eight tasks to be completed and you should complete every question.

The marks for each sub-task are shown alongside the task.

Read each task carefully before attempting the questions.

The VAT rate is 20%.

Task 1: 10 marks

(a)   Indicate in the table below whether the following statements relate to the memorandum of association or the articles of association.

	Memorandum of association	Articles of association
Document that is signed by all owners when the company is formed		
Document that highlights the purpose of the company and how it should be run		

(2 marks)

(b)   Indicate in the table below whether the following statements are true or false.

	True	False
Statutory books include details of people with significant control over a company		
Partnerships are run by shareholders and owned by directors		
If there are no changes to ownership of a limited company then you do not need to file a confirmation statement		
A sole trader can keep all of the profits they earn		

(4 marks)

(c)   Match the following activities to the correct function of the business, choosing from Sales and Marketing, Information Technology, Finance, Operations and Human Resources.

		Department
(a)	Promoting the services offered by the business	
(b)	Ensuring all software works across the organisation	
(c)	Recruitment of new staff	
(d)	Planning, control and performance improvement	

(4 marks)

Task 2: 13 marks

You work from 09.00 to 17.00, Monday to Friday of each week. Each finance period is four weeks in duration so you plan your work in a four week cycle.

The work schedules below show the days when routine tasks must be completed and the amount of time each task takes to complete. It is very important that you complete the management accounts tasks by the end of the identified day and the financial accounts tasks by the day and time indicated.

Monthly work schedule – management accounts					
	Monday	**Tuesday**	**Wednesday**	**Thursday**	**Friday**
Week 1	Variance analysis (2 hours)		Cost coding (3 hours)		
Week 2	Labour cost report (1 hour)	Labour cost report (1 hour)	Labour cost report (1 hour)		
Week 3	Data gathering (2 hours)	Material cost report (2 hours)	Product cost analysis (1 hour)	Product cost analysis (1 hour)	
Week 4	Data gathering (2 hours)			Budget report (2 hours)	Variance analysis (1 hour)

Weekly work schedule – financial accounts			
Task	**Task to be completed each week by:**		**Task duration**
	Day	**Time**	
Contact customers with outstanding debts	Monday	12.00	1 hour
Complete bank reconciliation	Wednesday	16:00	1 hour
Process purchase invoices	Tuesday	15:00	2 hours
Check emails and post cheques received	Every day	12.00	1 hour
Prepare payments to suppliers with remittance advices	Thursday	13:00	2 hours
Transfer entries from daybooks to ledgers	Friday	15:00	2 hours
Reconcile supplier statements	Wednesday	14:00	2 hours
Process sales invoices	Tuesday	16.00	2 hours

You are planning your work at the start of the day on Tuesday of week 2. You have been asked to complete a non-routine cash book task by 10am and lunch should be taken at 12pm to 1pm.

(a) Complete your to-do list for today, Tuesday of week 2. Refer to the management and financial accounts schedules and list the tasks in order of completion in the table set out below. Write the task descriptions in the column on the right.

Choose from the following tasks:

Product cost analysis	Cash book
Budget report	Cost coding
Process purchase invoices	Variance analysis
Complete bank reconciliation	Lunch
Labour cost report	Process sales invoices
Data gathering	Material cost report

Transfer entries from daybooks to ledgers

Check emails and post cheques received

Contact customers with outstanding debts

Prepare payments to suppliers with remittance advices

Reconcile supplier statements

Tuesday, week 2 to-do list (in order of completion)	
Task 1 09.00 -10.00	
Task 2 10.00 -11.00	
Task 3 11.00 -12.00	
Task 4 12.00 -13.00	
Task 5 13.00 -14.00	
Task 6 14.00 -15.00	
Task 7 15.00 -16.00	
Task 8 16.00 -17.00	

(4 marks)

You are often asked to complete non-routine tasks. However, two days in each of the four week cycles you are too busy with routine tasks to accept non-routine work.

(b) Identify on which days and in which week they fall in that you will be the busiest with routine tasks from the management and financial accounts schedules. Enter your answers into the table below.

Week number	Day of the week

Week number	Day of the week

(4 marks)

The finance function provides information to internal and external stakeholders.

(c)   Indicate in the table below whether the following stakeholders are internal or external.

	Internal	**External**
Bank		
Local community		
HMRC		
Business owner		
Employees		

(5 marks)

Task 3: 14 marks

The three situations below highlight breaches of ethical principles in the workplace.

(a)   Complete the table by entering the fundamental principle which is breached in each case. Choose from the following principles:

Integrity

Objectivity

Confidentiality

Professional competence and due care

Professional behaviour

(a)	A colleague uses some of the stamps purchased for the business to post her own personal mail	
(b)	The payroll assistant is heard in the local supermarket discussing colleagues pay rates	
(c)	The manager finds he is faced with a conflict of interest: his best friend's son is on the shortlist for a job and he is on the interviewing panel	
(d)	A colleague asks you to complete a tax return but you have never completed one before	

(4 marks)

Carlton Cycles is reviewing its sustainability policy.

(b)   Indicate in the table below which areas of sustainability the following statements refer to:

	Social	**Environmental**
Allow staff to volunteer in the community		
Use refillable ink cartridges for the office printer		
Run a care share scheme		
The use of fuel efficient cars		
Donation of profits to charity		
Reduce the amount of office printing		

(6 marks)

JHP Supplies is putting together a new corporate social responsibility (CSR) policy.

(c)   Identify which types of information should be included.

(a)	Improving working conditions for staff	
(b)	The updated payments policy	
(c)	The plan for improving safety measures which might win the business awards in the future	
(d)	How the business reduces its carbon footprint	
(e)	The business's guide on how to code transactions	
(f)	The authorisation limits on certain items of expenditure	
(g)	Plans for the business to work with the local community to raise funds for good causes	

(4 marks)

Task 4: 22 marks

This task is about processing transactions and communicating with customers and suppliers.

The Payables Ledger Supervisor, Mike Davies, has left you the following note today 10 August 20-X:

Note

We need to ask our supplier if we can extend our credit limit from £3,000 to £5,050. We have been trading with them for two years now and always pay our account on time.

The reason for this is because we would like to place a large order next month that would exceed our current credit limit. Here is our account information.

Contact name: Leo Brett

Supplier: Radford Supplies

Account number: CA001

Please could you send an email from yourself, as accounts assistant, to Leo Brett at Radford Supplies. Please explain the situation, include our account number and ask whether we can increase our credit limit in line with the figures above.

Thank you

Mike

(a)   Prepare an appropriate business email to Radford Supplies, making sure all the relevant information is included from the note above.

Email

To: lbrett@radfordsupplies.co.uk

From: accounts@carltoncyles.co.uk

Subject:

(6 marks)

Your colleague Meg is struggling to understand how the prompt payment discounts that the business takes from suppliers is recorded.

(b)   Indicate in the table below whether there is no impact, there should be a debit, or a credit for each of the account names listed.

Account name	No impact	Debit	Credit
Payables ledger control			
Receivables ledger control			
Discount received			
Discount allowed			

(4 marks)

She is also confused by the impact of invoicing a customer and the effect this has on the business.

(c)   Indicate in the table below whether there is no effect, a decrease or an increase for each transaction type.

Transaction type	No effect	Decrease	Increase
Expenses in the profit and loss			
Income in the profit and loss			
Assets in the balance sheet			
Liabilities in the balance sheet			

(4 marks)

(d)   Indicate in the table below whether the following accounts are assets or liabilities.

	Asset	Liability
Bank loan		
Amounts owed by HMRC		
Bank overdraft		
Inventory		

(4 marks)

Your colleague states that if you were using a digital bookkeeping system, everything would be easier?

(e)   Is he correct? Explain your answer.

(4 marks)

Task 5: 10 marks

This task is about using journals and reconciling a bank statement with the cash book.

You work for George Ltd. An error has been made in the accounts. An invoice from Radford Supplies has been incorrectly entered into the accounts of Radford Ltd.

(a) Indicate in the table below what type of error this is.

Type of error	
(a)	Error of commission	
(b)	Error of omission	
(c)	Error of principle	
(d)	Compensating error	

(1 mark)

On 1 August you receive the following bank statement.

BANK STATEMENT				
Date 20-7	Details	Paid out £	Paid in £	Balance £
01 Jul	Balance b/f			3,054 C
02 Jul	BACS credit: Ashford		2,000	5,054 C
07 Jul	BACS: JYB Supplies	600		4,454 C
09 Jul	Cheque 786355	560		3,894 C
10 Jul	BACS credit Proctor Ltd		900	4,794 C
12 Jul	Counter credit		525	5,319 C
15 Jul	Direct debit: First Electric	126		5,193 C
18 Jul	BACS credit: Watson Ltd		1,064	6,257 C
21 Jul	BACS credit: P Parker		1,030	7,287 C
22 Jul	Cheque 786357	68		7,219 C
25 Jul	Bank charges	11		7,208 C
25 Jul	Direct debit: PP Insure	29		7,179 C
25 Jul	Cheque 786358	77		7,102 C
D = Debit C = Credit				

(b) Enter any items into the cash book (on the next page) as needed. Total the cash book, clearly showing the balance carried down at 31 July and brought down at 1 August.

Select your entries for the details column from the following list: Balance b/d, Balance c/d, Bank charges, Closing balance, Ashford, First Electric, Watson Ltd, PP Insure, P Parker, Carlton Traders, T March, Brooklane, Ellie Ltd, Office rental, Newberry & Co, JYB Supplies, Opening balance, Proctor Ltd.

CASH BOOK

Date 20-7	Details	Bank £	Date 20-7	Cheque number	Details	Bank £
01-Jul	Balance b/f	3,054	05-Jul	786355	Watson Ltd	560
01-Jul	Ashford	2,000	15-Jul		First Electric	126
08-Jul	Carlton Traders	525	20-Jul	786356	Brooklane	605
21-Jul	P Parker	1,030	21-Jul	786357	Ellie Ltd	68
22-Jul	T March	890	23-Jul		Office rental	900
29-Jul	Ashford	50	23-Jul	786358	Newberry & Co	77

(5 marks)

(c) Complete the bank reconciliation statement as at 31 July.

Select your entries from the following list: Bank charges, Ashford, First Electric, Watson Ltd, P Parker, Carlton Traders, T March, Brooklane, Ellie Ltd, JYB Supplies, Office rental, PP Insure, Newberry & Co, Proctor Ltd.

Bank reconciliation statement	£
Balance as per bank statement	
Add	
Total to add	
Less	
Total to subtract	
Balance as per cash book	

(4 marks)

Task 6: 7 marks

This task relates to contract law.

(a) Complete the statement. 'The UK Parliament consists of .....':

(a)	House of Lords only	
(b)	House of Commons only	
(c)	The Reigning Monarch and the House of Lords	
(d)	The Reigning Monarch and the House of Commons	
(e)	The Reigning Monarch and the House of Lords and the House of Commons	

(1 mark)

(b) Indicate in the table below whether the following statements are true or false.

Statement		True	False
(a)	A counter offer does not terminate an original offer		
(b)	Once an offer has been accepted it can be revoked		

(2 marks)

(c) Indicate in the table below how the law is classified. Identify two correct answers.

(a)	Common law and civil law	
(b)	Criminal law and equity	
(c)	Civil law and common law	
(d)	Common law and equity	
(e)	Public law and civil law	
(f)	Common law and private law	

(2 marks)

(d) Indicate in the table below which of the following is the highest court.

(a)	Court of appeal	
(b)	UK Supreme Court	
(c)	High Court	
(d)	Crown Court	

(1 mark)

Tino Ltd has grown significantly over the last few months. It has entered into a contract with a local building firm to build a new warehouse which must be completed by the 31 December because stock has been ordered to arrive for January. There was a clause added into the contract with the builder that stated if the building was not completed by 31 December then there would be a charge of £2,000 a day.

Because of Covid, the builders didn't complete the building until 31 January. Tino Ltd had to pay additional storage costs of £20,000 and spend £5,000 redesigning all promotional materials.

(e) Select the maximum amount of damages that Tino Ltd could reclaim against the builders.

(a)	£25,000	
(b)	£62,000	
(c)	£0	
(d)	£87,000	

(1 mark)

Task 7: 10 marks

This task is about bookkeeping systems and the importance of information and data security.

Rainu runs a catering business. She has two employees and is struggling to recruit a third team member. This has led to her not invoicing clients on time and her accountant requires all accounting records to be submitted immediately as they are already overdue. Rainu thinks she will be okay to leave this for a while. She is thinking of getting a bank loan too.

(a) Which characteristics of useful information will this impact upon and what is the importance?

(3 marks)

Rainu records transactions manually and she has been thinking for a while about using accounting software.

(b) Suggest tasks Rainu could complete if she used digital technology.

(4 marks)

(c) Suggest three advantages of Rainu using cloud-based accounting systems.

(3 marks)

Task 8: 14 marks

This task relates to the external business environment.

(a) Indicate in the table below whether the following statements are an advantage or disadvantage of a business trading internationally.

Statement		Advantage	Disadvantage
(a)	Difficult to predict finances with currencies fluctuating		
(b)	Each country has its own taxes		
(c)	Risk is spread if the business operates internationally		
(d)	Acquiring technical knowledge from working internationally		

(4 marks)

(b) Indicate in the table below whether the following are effects from a competitive global market.

(a)	Lower costs	
(b)	Economies of scale	
(c)	Lower profit margins	
(d)	Higher wage costs	
(e)	Higher profit margins	

(3 marks)

(c) Indicate in the table below whether the following statements are true or false.

Statements		True	False
(a)	A change in exchange rates will impact upon a business even if you do not buy or sell goods overseas		
(b)	During a recession, the government wants lower interest rates		
(c)	A business in the UK that exports goods will not benefit from a fall in the value of the pound		

(3 marks)

(d)   Complete the following sentences by choosing the correct words from the boxes below.

Increase		Decrease

(1)   Savers will be encouraged to save more when interest rates ....

(2)   People may spend more rather than save when interest rates ....

(3)   Borrowers may borrow more when interest rates ....

(4)   Borrowers may be discouraged from borrowing money when interest rates ....

(4 marks)

Answers to practice synoptic assessment 1

Task 1: 10 marks

(a)

Statement	True	False
A sole trader is also referred to as 'self-employed'	✔	
Income Tax applies to individuals only	✔	
Corporation Tax applies to partnerships only		✔

(Note: 1 mark for each correct answer, total of 3 marks)

(b)

Statement	True	False
You will need to identify and decide who will be classed as 'people with significant control' (PSC) over your business	✔	
You can choose any business name		✔
You should have one guarantor and one shareholder		✔
You should choose a director of the company who can also be a shareholder	✔	

(Note: 1 mark for each correct answer, total of 4 marks)

(c)

(a)	You can choose the company name	
(b)	All legal documents are provided	✔
(c)	Quicker to set up	✔

(Note: 1 mark for each correct answer, total of 2 marks)

(d)

Stakeholder		
(a)	HM Revenue & Customs	✔
(b)	Directors	
(c)	Staff	

(1 mark)

Task 2: 13 marks

(a)

Thursday, week 2 to-do list (in order of completion)	
Task 1 09.00 -10.00	Petty cash book
Task 2 10.00 -11.00	Labour cost report
Task 3 11.00 -12.00	Check emails and post cheques
Task 4 12.00 -13.00	Reconcile supplier statements
Task 5 13.00 -14.00	Reconcile supplier statements

Notes: Can also accept Task 2 Check emails and post cheques and Task 3 Labour cost report.

Can also accept doing the Labour cost report last and moving the other tasks one step up.

(1 mark for each correct answer, total of 4 marks)

(b)

Week number	Day of the week
1	Monday

(Note: 1 mark for each correct answer, total of 2 marks)

(c)

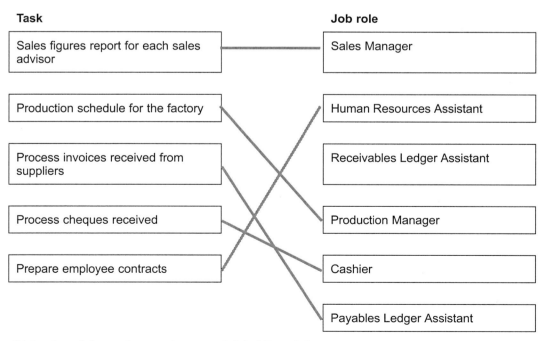

Task	Job role
Sales figures report for each sales advisor	Sales Manager
Production schedule for the factory	Human Resources Assistant
Process invoices received from suppliers	Receivables Ledger Assistant
Process cheques received	Production Manager
Prepare employee contracts	Cashier
	Payables Ledger Assistant

(Note: 1 mark for each correct answer, total of 5 marks)

(d)

Statement	Sales	Marketing
The cost of promoting goods for sale on Facebook		✔
The revenue generated from sales received through Facebook advertisements	✔	

(Note: 1 mark for each correct answer, total of 2 marks)

Task 3: 14 marks

JYB Supplies is reviewing its sustainability policy.

(a) Select which areas of sustainability the following statements refer to.

	Social	Environmental
Using resources that can be reused		✔
Supporting colleagues	✔	
Reduction of emissions		✔
Reducing the quantity of printing		✔
Donation of profits to charity	✔	
Offering a cycle to work incentive scheme		✔
Energy saving schemes		✔

(7 marks)

(b)

Situation	Ethical principle
Your colleague asks you whether you are working on their parent's accounts and to tell them whether they made a profit in the year	Confidentiality
Your manager is off sick. Your colleague needs you to complete a tax return. You have never received training as to how to complete a tax return	Professional competence and due care
You are responsible for collating monthly expense receipts. Your colleague said they left a receipt for work travel at a friend's house and can you process it and they will pass you the receipt next week	Integrity

(3 marks)

(c)

	True	False
It is never acceptable in any circumstance to disclose confidential information		✔

(1 mark)

(d)

	True	False
If a business adopts sustainable measures, it will save money		✔
Moving to cloud-based accounting and not printing invoices and purchase orders is a sustainable measure	✔	
Government schemes are available to help towards the cost of businesses reducing emissions	✔	

(3 marks)

Task 4: 22 marks

(a)   Errors on purchase invoice:
- Net total is incorrect. It should be £420.00. *(1 mark)*
- The VAT has been deducted instead of added. This impacts on the invoice total, which should be £504.00. *(1 mark)*

Errors on purchase credit note:
- Wrong trade discount percentage applied (it states 20% but 10% has been applied). *(1 mark)*
- The number of items returned do not match (quantity states 12 but reason for credit states two). *(1 mark)*

(Note: Total of 4 marks)

(b)   (c)   Purchases daybook *(1 mark)*

(c)

Date 20-X	Supplier code	Supplier	General ledger code	Invoice number	Net £	VAT code
29 July	**PW001**	**PWS Suppliers**	5000	INV4514	124.44	V4
30 July	WO001	Working Products	5000	269852	494.10	V4

(Note: 1 mark for each correct answer, total of 11 marks)

(d)

JYB Supplies

410 Wrenthorpe Industrial Estate

Clifton, CL47 6KU

Mr Jones

Carlton Homeworld

Newmarket Lane

Burton

BF5 8JK

2 June 20-X

Dear Mr Jones/Sir

Overdue Account

I am writing to you regarding your overdue account of £9,500. The payment terms on your account are 30 days.

The outstanding amount relates to invoice number 451 dated 1 April 20-X.

Please can you arrange payment by return? However, if you have any questions or queries, please do not hesitate to contact me.

Yours sincerely/faithfully

Tina Brett

Finance Manager

Note: To access the higher marks in the band, the answer must include all criteria in the band. Those students that include only some of the additional criteria in a band should be awarded the lower mark.

Where applicable, dates within the body of the letter need not include the year.

Marks	Descriptor
0	No response worthy of credit.
1-2	– There is some form of opening salutation and complimentary close, although they are not necessarily consistent with each other. – The body of the letter is sufficiently grammatically correct to communicate the message that: – an amount is overdue/outstanding – payment is required by return – The letter, including the opening salutation and complimentary close, may contain spelling errors.
3-4	– The letter is dated, including the year, and has an appropriate heading. – The opening salutation and complimentary close are appropriate and consistent with each other. – Tina Brett's name is shown below the complimentary close. – The spelling and grammar within the body of the letter are sufficiently correct to communicate the message that: – an amount of £9,500 is overdue/outstanding – the customer should contact Tina Brett to discuss any queries or forward payment by return
5-6	– The letter is dated, including the year, and has an appropriate heading. – The opening salutation and complimentary close are appropriate and consistent with each other. – Tina Brett's name and job title are shown below the complimentary close. – The body of the letter is well structured, with spelling and grammar that is mainly correct and communicates the message that: – an amount of £9,500 is overdue/outstanding – the amount overdue/outstanding relates to invoice number 451 dated 1 April 20-X – the customer should contact Tina Brett to discuss any queries or forward payment by return

Task 5: 10 marks

(a)

Account name	Amount £	Debit	Credit
Entry from the purchase daybook	5,448		✔
Entry from the purchase returns daybook	960	✔	

(Note: 1 mark for each correct answer, total of 4 marks)

(b)

Amount £	Debit	Credit
5,268	✔	

Workings: £5,410 + £5,448 – £4,630 – £960 = £5,268

(Note: 1 mark for each correct answer, total of 2 marks)

(c)

Reconciliation statement	Amount £
Receivables ledger control account balance	29,463
Total of the receivables ledger balances	29,016
Difference	447

(Note: 1 mark for each correct answer, total of 2 marks)

(d) A receipt was entered twice in a customer's account in the receivables ledger

An invoice was entered twice in the receivables ledger control account

(Note: 1 mark for each correct answer, total of 2 marks)

Task 6: 7 marks

(a)

	Civil law	Criminal law
Fraud		✔
Money laundering		✔
Breach of contract	✔	

(Note: 1 mark for each correct answer, total of 3 marks)

(b)

	True	False
An invitation to treat is an offer		✔
A valid contract is legally binding	✔	
A void contract can be enforced by law		✔

(Note: 1 mark for each correct answer, total of 3 marks)

(c)

(a)	Yes, because the message had been sent to Josie and Josie should have acknowledged it	
(b)	No, because Josie did not reply to Jasmin's offer, and therefore did not accept it	✔
(c)	Yes, because Josie should have told Jasmin she was not accepting the offer	

(Note: 1 mark for each correct answer, total of 1 mark)

Task 7: 10 marks

(a)

> Implications for the business
>
> - Reputation risk that he is not protecting the data of his clients
> - Financial loss if he is fined
> - Risk of clients taking legal action against him
>
> Steps he should take to avoid this happening again
>
> - Let the clients know there has been a breach of data and what data he held about them
> - Ensure there is two-step verification which would have stopped someone being able to gain access to the information
>
> *(Note: 1 mark for each correct answer. Any other valid answer should be awarded but maximum marks of 5 available)*

(b)

(a)	Email the file as it is	
(b)	Password protect the file with a filename that is easy to remember such as 123	
(c)	Password protect the file with a password that contains a combination of upper and lower case letters and symbols	✔

(Note: 1 mark for each correct answer, total of 1 mark)

(c)

> - Real-time updates
> - Collaborative working with his new employee
> - Cost effective as saves the business time
>
> *(Note: 1 mark for each correct answer. Any other valid answer should be awarded but maximum marks of 3 available)*

(d)

(a)	Give him the Director's work mobile number instead	
(b)	Give him the number to ensure the company gets paid	
(c)	Give out the email address instead	
(d)	Refer to your supervisor as this is confidential information you are being asked to disclose	✔

(Note: 1 mark for each correct answer, total of 1 mark)

Task 8: 14 marks

(a)

(a)	Yes	✔
(b)	No	

(Note: 1 mark for each correct answer, total of 1 mark)

(b)

Statement	True	False
The threat of fraud is an example of a compliance risk		✔
Political uncertainties are outside of our control?	✔	
Changes in interest rates is an example of a political risk?		✔
Facing legal proceedings is an example of compliance risk	✔	

(Note: 1 mark for each correct answer, total of 4 marks)

(c)

(a)	Boom	✔
(b)	Recession	

(Note: 1 mark for each correct answer, total of 1 mark)

(d)

Statement	True	False
A trade deficit occurs when imports exceed exports		✔

(Note: 1 mark for each correct answer, total of 1 mark)

(e)

(a)	Slow economic growth	✔
(b)	Increase in consumer spending	

(Note: 1 mark for each correct answer, total of 1 mark)

(f)

Statement	True	False
High inflation results in consumers spending less	✔	
Deflation is often referred to as negative inflation	✔	

(Note: 1 mark for each correct answer, total of 2 marks)

(g)

Statement	True	False
Technology issues relating to not keeping software up-to-date is an internal risk to the business	✔	
Labour shortages due to not having the correctly skilled workforce is an external risk		✔
New technology that could make your business's technology obsolete is an example of an external risk	✔	
Fluctuations in exchange rates is an example of an external risk	✔	

(Note: 1 mark for each correct answer, total of 4 marks)

Answers to practice synoptic assessment 2

Task 1: 10 marks

(a)

		Sole Trader	Limited Company	Partnership	Not-for-profit
(a)	Difficult to take time off	✔			
(b)	Shares the profit and responsibilities			✔	
(c)	Controlled by shareholders		✔		
(d)	Set up to make an impact rather than make a profit				✔
(e)	With this ownership, if the owner is ill, the business may have to cease trading	✔			

(Note: 1 mark for each correct answer, total of 5 marks)

(b)

		True	False
(a)	A pre-incorporation contract is a contract entered into before a company has been legally formed	✔	
(b)	A pre-incorporation contract must be in writing	✔	

(Note: 1 mark for each correct answer, total of 2 marks)

(c)

Statement		Correct	Incorrect
(a)	If I convert to a limited company from a sole trader, I will have to pay Corporation Tax through my business	✔	
(b)	I will need directors and shareholders	✔	
(c)	Shareholders will not have limited liability		✔

(Note: 1 mark for each correct answer, total of 3 marks)

Task 2: 13 marks

(a)

(a)	Stock valuation	
(b)	Chasing customers for payment	✔
(c)	Banking cheques received	✔
(d)	Being able to work to deadlines	

(Note: 1 mark for each correct answer, total of 2 marks)

(b)   (a)   Customers pay earlier *(1 mark)*

(c)

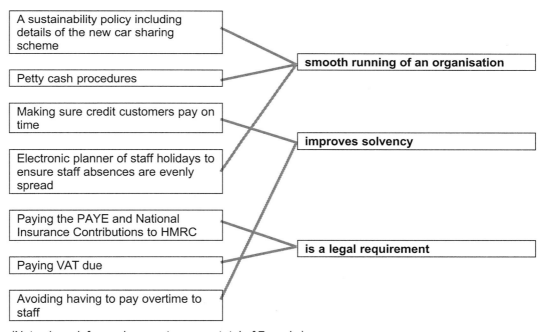

(Note: 1 mark for each correct answer, total of 7 marks)

(d)

(a)	Meeting tax deadlines	✔
(b)	Not keeping the payroll records up-to-date	
(c)	Knowing the day-to-day running costs of the business	✔
(d)	Completing a Microsoft Excel course	

(Note: 1 mark for each correct answer, total of 2 marks)

(e)

(a)	Promote someone from within the business by advertising the role internally	
(b)	Advertise the post externally	
(c)	Outsource the payroll function to a specialist company	✔

(1 mark)

Task 3: 14 marks

(a)

(a)	Driving for two hours to attend a meeting	
(b)	Holding a meeting via skype	✔
(c)	Using recyclable plant holders	✔
(d)	Ensuring customers are treated equally	
(e)	Promoting a cycle to work scheme	✔
(f)	Printing all accounting correspondence and filing in the accounts office	

(Note: 1 mark for each correct answer, total of 3 marks)

(b)

(a)	Integrity	✔
(b)	Objectivity	✔
(c)	Confidence	
(d)	Effectiveness	
(e)	Professional competence and due care	✔
(f)	Motivation	

(Note: 1 mark for each correct answer, total of 3 marks)

(c)

(a)	Not providing the time off for a member of staff to attend an AAT course	
(b)	Sponsoring a local charity bike ride	✔
(c)	Buying supplies from the cheapest supplier possible	
(d)	Recycling packaging used on deliveries	✔
(e)	Restricting the use of the internet at work for social networking	
(f)	Allowing staff time off to volunteer at the local school summer fayre	✔
(g)	Running the heating at a low level all year	✔

(Note: 1 mark for each correct answer, total of 4 marks)

(d)   An accounting technician should comply with the AAT's Code of **Professional Ethics**.

An accounting technician has a **public interest duty** to their employer, clients and society.

Complying with **regulations** may not constitute ethical behaviour.

(Note: 1 mark for each correct answer, total of 3 marks)

(e)

(a)	Process the transaction as without this job you cannot pay your mortgage	
(b)	Contact the AAT for advice	✔
(c)	Speak to your colleague who has been claiming the mileage	

(1 mark)

Task 4: 22 marks

(a)

> **Brooklane Garden Centre**
>
> 28 Steinbeck Street
>
> Granby, BG3 8JY
>
>
> Mr Templin
>
> Sleaford Supplies
>
> Coulby Lane
>
> Granby
>
> BH8 5GH
>
> 3rd July 20-X
>
>
> Dear Mr Templin/Sir,
>
> **Credit note**
>
> I am writing to you regarding our recently returned two sets of garden furniture.
>
> It appears on credit note 542 dated 20th June 20-X you have only credited us for one set of garden furniture. However, we returned two sets. The credit note has also been omitted from your statement.
>
> Please can you send us a revised credit note and statement?
>
> If you have any questions or queries, please do not hesitate to contact me.
>
> Yours sincerely/faithfully,
>
>
>
> Chris Brian
>
> Finance Manager

Note: To access the higher marks in the band, the answer must include all criteria in the band. Those students that include only some of the additional criteria in a band should be awarded the lower mark.

Where applicable, dates within the body of the letter need not include the year.

Marks	*Descriptor*
0	*No response worthy of credit.*

1-2	– *There is some form of opening salutation and complimentary close, although they are not necessarily consistent with each other.*
	
	– *The body of the letter is sufficiently grammatically correct to communicate the message that:*
	
	    – *the incorrect credit note has been mentioned*
	
	    – *the incorrect statement has been mentioned*
	
	– *The letter, including the opening salutation and complimentary close, may contain spelling errors.*

3-4	– *The letter is dated, including the year, and has an appropriate heading.*
	
	– *The opening salutation and complimentary close are appropriate and consistent with each other.*
	
	– *Chris Brian's name is shown below the complimentary close.*
	
	– *The spelling and grammar within the body of the letter are sufficiently correct to communicate the message that:*
	
	    – *credit note 542 dated 20 June is incorrect*
	
	    – *the supplier should contact Chris Brian to discuss any queries and issue a revised credit note and statement*

5-6	– *The letter is dated, including the year, and has an appropriate heading.*
	
	– *The opening salutation and complimentary close are appropriate and consistent with each other.*
	
	– *Chris Brian's name and job title are shown below the complimentary close.*
	
	– *The body of the letter is well structured, with spelling and grammar that is mainly correct and communicates the message that:*
	
	    – *credit note 542 should have been for two sets of garden furniture, not one set*
	
	    – *the statement issued is also incorrect*
	
	    – *the supplier should contact Chris Brian to discuss any queries and issue a revised credit note and statement*

(b)

(a)	Sales daybook	
(b)	Purchase returns daybook	✔
(c)	Purchases daybook	
(d)	Sales returns daybook	

(1 mark)

(c)

Date 20-X	Supplier code	Supplier	General ledger code	Credit note number	Net £	VAT code
30 July	WDB012	Woodborough Ltd	5012	CN067	140.00	V4
31 July	YNS002	LYB Newton & Son Ltd	5012	01240	783.36	V4
		Totals			923.36	

(Note: 1 mark for each correct line, total of 14 marks. Marks are not awarded for total figures)

(d)

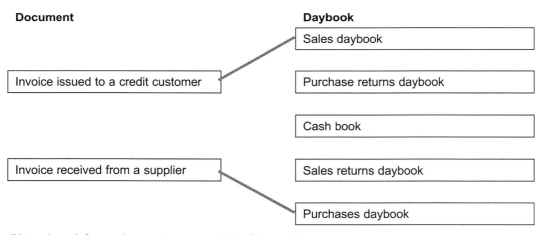

(Note: 1 mark for each correct answer, total of 2 marks)

Task 5: 10 marks

(a)   (1)   **Journal**

Account name	Amount £	Debit	Credit
Irrecoverable debts	2,982.75	✔	
VAT	596.55	✔	
Receivables ledger control	3,579.30		✔

(Note: 1 mark for each correct line of the journal, total of 3 marks)

(2)

	Will cause an imbalance	Will not cause an imbalance
The vehicle expenses have been debited with £12,451. This should have been posted to the vehicles account		✔
The balance on the rent received account has been calculated incorrectly	✔	

(Note: 1 mark for each correct answer, total of 2 marks)

(b)

Account name	Original balance £	Debit	Credit
Purchase returns	2,906		✔
VAT Control (owing to HMRC)	5,680		✔
Bank interest received	58		✔
Bank (overdrawn bank balance)	3,970		✔
Sales returns	585	✔	

(Note: 1 mark for each correct answer, total of 5 marks)

Task 6: 7 marks

(a)

		Common law	Equity
(a)	The only possible remedy is damages	✔	
(b)	Concerned about fairness		✔
(c)	Introduced remedies such as injunctions		✔

(Note: 1 mark for each correct answer, total of 3 marks)

(b)

		Public law	Private law
(a)	This law deals with matters such as social welfare across the UK	✔	
(b)	This law focuses on enforcing the law between individuals		✔
(c)	This law can include company law		✔

(Note: 1 mark for each correct answer, total of 3 marks)

(c)

(a)	Yes	
(b)	No	✔

(1 mark)

Task 7: 10 marks

(a)

(a)	Timely	✔
(b)	Comparable	
(c)	Consistent	
(d)	Relevant	

(1 mark)

(b)

		Purchase order	Statement	Remittance advice	Invoice
(a)	This is completed when goods are ordered	✔			
(b)	This advises when payment is made			✔	
(c)	This shows how much money is owed at the end of month		✔		
(d)	This shows how much is owed for a specific order and the date it should be paid				✔

(Note: 1 mark for each correct answer, total of 4 marks)

(c)

(a)	Check the app developer's website	✔
(b)	Notify the client	
(c)	Speak to your manager	✔
(d)	Ignore it as it may be fake news	
(e)	Suggest a new software	

(Note: 1 mark for each correct answer, total of 2 marks)

(d)

(a)	Make sure passwords are memorable and simple to remember such as your date of birth	
(b)	Everyone should have access to the whole computer systems	
(c)	The cloud will automatically back up your PC	
(d)	You will need to ensure that each software you use is backed up	✔
(e)	You should use passwords that contain a mixture of upper case, lower case, letters, numbers and special characters	✔
(f)	You should restrict staff access to the areas they need to use in the software they have access to	✔

(Note: 1 mark for each correct answer, total of 3 marks)

Task 8: 14 marks

(a)

		True	False
(a)	If Gross Domestic Product (GDP) increases, the standard of living should improve	✔	
(b)	If Gross Domestic Product (GDP) increases, this is a sign of economic strength	✔	
(c)	If exports exceed imports, there will be a trade deficit		✔

(Note: 1 mark for each correct answer, total of 3 marks)

(b)

(a)	Fairness	✔
(b)	Efficiency	
(c)	Convenience	✔
(d)	Effectiveness	

(Note: 1 mark for each correct answer, total of 2 marks)

(c)

		Direct	Indirect
(a)	Income Tax	✔	
(b)	Inheritance Tax	✔	
(c)	Council Tax		✔

(Note: 1 mark for each correct answer, total of 3 marks)

(d)

		Boom	Recession	Slowdown	Recovery
(a)	Where GDP is in decline for two consecutive quarters		✔		
(b)	An upturn in the economy	✔			
(c)	The stage of the economic cycle that follows recession				✔
(d)	When the rate of the economic growth decelerates			✔	

(Note: 1 mark for each correct answer, total of 4 marks)

(e)

	Increased	Decreased
If the demand for expensive items increases and there is a decrease in demand for basic items, does this mean consumer income has increased or decreased?	✔	

(1 mark)

	Strong currency	Weak currency
If a business finds imports are more expensive than exports, this is a sign of what?		✔

(1 mark)

Answers to practice synoptic assessment 3

Task 1: 10 marks

(a)

	Memorandum of association	Articles of association
Document that is signed by all owners when the company is formed	✔	
Document that highlights the purpose of the company and how it should be run		✔

(Note: 1 mark for each correct answer, total of 2 marks)

(b)

	True	False
Statutory books include details of people with significant control over a company	✔	
Partnerships are run by shareholders and owned by directors		✔
If there are no changes to ownership of a limited company then you do not need to file a confirmation statement		✔
A sole trader can keep all of the profits they earn	✔	

(Note: 1 mark for each correct answer, total of 4 marks)

(c)

		Department
(a)	Promoting the services offered by the business	Sales and Marketing
(b)	Ensuring all software works across the organisation	Information Technology
(c)	Recruitment of new staff	Human Resources
(d)	Planning, control and performance improvement	Operations

(Note: 1 mark for each correct answer, total of 4 marks)

Task 2: 13 marks

(a)

Tuesday, week 2 to-do list (in order of completion)	
Task 1 09.00 -10.00	Cash book
Task 2 10.00 -11.00	Check emails and post cheques received
Task 3 11.00 -12.00	Process purchase invoices
Task 4 12.00 -13.00	Lunch
Task 5 13.00 -14.00	Process purchase invoices
Task 6 14.00 -15.00	Process sales invoices
Task 7 15.00 -16.00	Process sales invoices
Task 8 16.00 -17.00	Labour cost report

(Note: ½ mark for each correct answer, total of 4 marks)

(b)

Week number	Day of the week
1	Wednesday

Week number	Day of the week
3	Tuesday

(Note: 1 mark for each correct answer, total of 4 marks)

(c)

	Internal	External
Bank		✔
Local community		✔
HMRC		✔
Business owner	✔	
Employees	✔	

(Note: 1 mark for each correct answer, total of 5 marks)

Task 3: 14 marks

(a)

(a)	A colleague uses some of the stamps purchased for the business to post her own personal mail	**Integrity**
(b)	The payroll assistant is heard in the local supermarket discussing colleagues pay rates	**Confidentiality**
(c)	The manager finds he is faced with a conflict of interest: his best friend's son is on the shortlist for a job and he is on the interviewing panel	**Objectivity**
(d)	A colleague asks you to complete a tax return but you have never completed one before	**Professional competence and due care**

(Note: 1 mark for each correct answer, total of 4 marks)

(b)

	Social	Environmental
Allow staff to volunteer in the community	✔	
Use refillable ink cartridges for the office printer		✔
Run a car share scheme		✔
The use of fuel efficient cars		✔
Donation of profits to charity	✔	
Reduce the amount of office printing		✔

(Note: 1 mark for each correct answer, total of 6 marks)

(c)

(a)	Improving working conditions for staff	✔
(b)	The updated payments policy	
(c)	The plan for improving safety measures which might win the business awards in the future	✔
(d)	How the business reduces its carbon footprint	✔
(e)	The business's guide on how to code transactions	
(f)	The authorisation limits on certain items of expenditure	
(g)	Plans for the business to work with the local community to raise funds for good causes	✔

(Note: 1 mark for each correct answer, total of 4 marks)

Task 4: 22 marks

(a)

Email	
To:	lbrett@radfordsupplies.co.uk
From:	accounts@carltoncycles.co.uk
Subject:	Credit limit

Hello Leo,

Purchase Account number CA001

Our credit limit is currently £3,000. Would it be possible to extend this to £5,050 please? We have been trading with you for over two years and always pay our account on time.

Next month, we would like to place a large order with you that exceeds our current credit limit.

If you have any questions or queries, please do not hesitate to contact me.

Kind regards

Accounts Assistant

Note: To access the higher marks in the band, the answer must include all criteria in the band. Those students that include only some of the additional criteria in a band should be awarded the lower mark.

Where applicable dates within the body of the email need not include the year.

Marks	Descriptor
0	*No response worthy of credit.*
1-2	– *There is some form of opening salutation and complimentary close which are both appropriate for an email sent to a supplier.* – *The body of the email is sufficiently grammatically correct to communicate the message that:* – *the business would like to increase its credit limit* – *the business has been trading with the supplier for over two years and always pays its account on time* – *The email, including the opening salutation and complimentary close, may contain spelling errors.*
3-4	– *The email 'subject' has been completed appropriately.* – *There is an opening salutation which is appropriate for an email sent to a supplier.* – *There is a complimentary close, which may or may not include a name, but must include the position 'Accounts Assistant' and is appropriate for an email sent to a supplier.* – *The spelling and grammar within the body of the email is sufficiently correct to communicate the following message:* – *asked whether it is possible to extend the credit limit from £3,000 to £5,050 and informed them that we have held an account for over two years*
5-6	– *The email 'subject' has been completed appropriately.* – *There is an opening salutation which is appropriate for an email sent to a supplier.* – *There is a complimentary close, which may or may not include a name, but must include the position 'Accounts Assistant' and is appropriate for an email sent to a supplier.* – *The body of the email is well structured, with spelling and grammar that is mainly correct and communicates the following messages:* – *asked whether it is possible to extend the credit limit from £3,000 to £5,050 and informed them that we have held an account for over two years* – *included that we would like to place a large order that exceeds our current credit limit.*

(b)

Account name	No impact	Debit	Credit
Payables ledger control		✔	
Receivables ledger control	✔		
Discount received			✔
Discount allowed	✔		

(Note: 1 mark for each correct answer, total of 4 marks)

(c)

Transaction type	No effect	Decrease	Increase
Expenses in the profit and loss	✔		
Income in the profit and loss			✔
Assets in the balance sheet			✔
Liabilities in the balance sheet	✔		

(Note: 1 mark for each correct answer, total of 4 marks)

(d)

	Asset	Liability
Bank loan		✔
Amounts owed by HMRC	✔	
Bank overdraft		✔
Inventory	✔	

(Note: 1 mark for each correct answer, total of 4 marks)

(e)

Yes, he is correct.

The accounting software has a code for each transaction which is classified into assets, liabilities, equity, income and expenditure.

You can use apps that will scan invoices and automatically code them.

It will also automatically reconcile bank transactions.

(Note: 1 mark for each correct answer, total of 4 marks. Also accept any other reasonable answer)

Task 5: 10 marks

(a)

Type of error	
(a) Error of commission	✔
(b) Error of omission	
(c) Error of principle	
(d) Compensating error	

(Note: total of 1 mark)

(b)

CASH BOOK

Date 20-7	Details	Bank £	Date 20-7	Cheque number	Details	Bank £
01-Jul	Balance b/f	3,054	05-Jul	786355	Watson Ltd	560
01-Jul	Ashford	2,000	15-Jul		First Electric	126
08-Jul	Carlton Traders	525	20-Jul	786356	Brooklane	605
21-Jul	P Parker	1,030	21-Jul	786357	Ellie Ltd	68
22-Jul	T March	890	23-Jul		Office Rental	900
29-Jul	Ashford	50	23-Jul	786358	Newberry & Co	77
10-Jul	**Proctor Ltd**	**900**	**07-Jul**		**JYB Supplies**	**600**
18-Jul	**Watson Ltd**	**1,064**	**25-Jul**		**Bank charges**	**11**
			25-Jul		**PP Insure**	**29**
			31-Jul		**Balance c/d**	**6,537**
		9,513				**9,513**
01-Aug	**Balance b/d**	**6,537**				

(Note: ½ mark for each correct transaction entered, ½ mark for each £9,513 and 1 mark for the final balance b/d of £6,537. Total of 5 marks)

(c)

Bank reconciliation statement	£
Balance as per bank statement	7,102
Add	
T March	890
Ashford	50
Total to add	940
Less	
Brooklane	605
Office Rental	900
Total to subtract	1,505
Balance as per cash book	6,537

(Note: ½ mark for each correct row entered, total of 4 marks)

Task 6: 7 marks

(a)

(a)	House of Lords only	
(b)	House of Commons only	
(c)	The Reigning Monarch and the House of Lords	
(d)	The Reigning Monarch and the House of Commons	
(e)	The Reigning Monarch and the House of Lords and the House of Commons	✔

(Note: 1 mark for each correct answer)

(b)

Statement		True	False
(a)	A counter offer does not terminate an original offer		✔
(b)	Once an offer has been accepted it can be revoked		✔

(Note: 1 mark for each correct answer, total of 2 marks)

(c)

(a)	Common law and civil law	
(b)	Criminal law and equity	
(c)	Civil law and common law	✔
(d)	Common law and equity	✔
(e)	Public law and civil law	
(f)	Common law and private law	

(Note: 1 mark for each correct answer, total of 2 marks)

(d)

(a)	Court of appeal	
(b)	UK Supreme Court	✔
(c)	High Court	
(d)	Crown Court	

(Note: 1 mark for each correct answer)

(e)

(a)	£25,000	
(b)	£62,000	✔
(c)	£0	
(d)	£87,000	

(Note: 1 mark for each correct answer)

Task 7: 10 marks

(a)   Reliability *(1 mark)* – assumes information is accurate and up-to-date; and relevance to help make decisions. *(Accept any other reasonable answers with a total of 3 marks)*

(b)   Invoicing catering clients

Paying suppliers

Logging expenses

Bank reconciliation

(Note: 1 mark for each correct answer, total of 4 marks. Accept any other reasonable answer)

(c)   Quick to update

More efficient

Real-time data

(Note: 1 mark for each correct answer, total of 3 marks. Accept any other reasonable answer)

Task 8: 14 marks

(a)

Statement		Advantage	Disadvantage
(a)	Difficult to predict finances with currencies fluctuating		✔
(b)	Each country has its own taxes		✔
(c)	Risk is spread if the business operates internationally	✔	
(d)	Acquiring technical knowledge from working internationally	✔	

(Note: 1 mark for each correct answer, total of 4 marks)

(b)

(a)	Lower costs	✔
(b)	Economies of scale	✔
(c)	Lower profit margins	
(d)	Higher wage costs	
(e)	Higher profit margins	✔

(Note: 1 mark for each correct answer, total of 3 marks)

(c)

Statements		True	False
(a)	A change in exchange rates will impact upon a business even if you do not buy or sell goods overseas	✔	
(b)	During a recession the government wants lower interest rates	✔	
(c)	A business in the UK that exports goods will not benefit from a fall in the value of a pound		✔

(Note: 1 mark for each correct answer, total of 3 marks)

(d) **(1)** Savers will be encouraged to save more when interest rates **increase**

(2) People may spend more rather than save when interest rates **decrease**

(3) Borrowers may borrow more when interest rates **decrease**

(4) Borrowers may be discouraged from borrowing money when interest rates **increase**

(Note: 1 mark for each correct answer, total of 4 marks)

for your notes

for your notes